Applying
Statistical
Concepts

DAVID A. CORNS
9212 Barbara Lane
Fort Wayne, Indiana 46804
219/432-0446

Applying Statistical Concepts

A Workbook to Accompany

Applied Statistics for the Behavioral Sciences

by Dennis E. Hinkle,
William Wiersma,
Stephen G. Jurs

Prepared by Dennis E. Hinkle,
Virginia Polytechnic Institute and State University

John R. Cox,
Virginia Polytechnic Institute and State University

Larry E. Ewing,
Virginia Western Community College

Rand McNally College Publishing Company/Chicago

Sponsoring editor: Louise Waller
Project editor: Frederick S. Smith
Designer: James Buddenbaum

79 80 81 10 9 8 7 6 5 4 3 2
Copyright © 1979 by Rand McNally College Publishing Company
Printed in U.S.A.

Contents

Preface

This workbook will serve to help students refine their knowledge and understanding of the basic statistical procedures used in research in the behavioral sciences. In addition, students will have an opportunity to perfect their computational skills when carrying out these statistical procedures.

The subject content of the workbook chapters parallels that of the textbook. Each chapter is divided into three sections: (1) a narrative review of the concepts in each chapter; (2) a set of exercises related to these concepts; (3) a mastery test.

In the narrative review, numbered blanks replace words or phrases that reflect major concepts. By supplying the missing words, students play an active role in reviewing these concepts. Answers are provided at the end of each narrative review section.

The exercise section supplements the exercises in the textbook and is designed to assist students in working typical problems. The format of the exercises is structured logically in order to maximize the students' understanding of statistical procedures and, most importantly, of the underlying concepts. Hints are sometimes provided to remind students of what they have learned in the textbook and to guide them through potential problem areas. Step-by-step solutions and answers follow each exercise section.

A mastery test is included at the end of each set of exercises. Tests include items that deal both with key concepts and with computational procedures. Again, answers follow.

The authors of the workbook are confident that students will find these materials helpful in their study of statistics. The exercise sections, which directly supplement corresponding textbook presentations, should be completed on an ongoing, day-to-day basis. The opening narratives and mastery tests, however, can serve a future as well as immediate purpose by structuring the students' review prior to examinations.

D. E. H.
J. R. C.
L. E. E.

1 Introduction

Comprehension Check

(1) data
(2) numbers (value)
(3) variable
(4) constant
(5) continuous
(6) discrete
(7) any
(8) scale
(9) interval (designated)
(10) independent
(11) dependent
(12) independent
(13) values (levels)
(14) data (treatments)
(15) dependent
(16) depends
(17) categories (numbers)
(18) precision
(19) nominal
(20) exclusive
(21) order (ing)
(22) ordinal
(23) order
(24) ranked (scaled)

The following summary reviews the material presented in this chapter. To check your understanding of key concepts, supply the missing words indicated by the numbered blanks.

The word statistics, to the researcher in the behavioral sciences, means the procedures used to enhance our understanding of ___(1)___ . Data are some characteristics of individuals or things that can be assigned a ___(2)___. A characteristic that can take on different values for different members of the group under study is called a ___(3)___ . If a characteristic has the same value for all members of the group under study, it is called a ___(4)___ . Variables can be categorized as either ___(5)___ variables or ___(6)___ variables. A continuous variable is one that can take ___(7)___ value on the measurement ___(8)___ under consideration. A discrete variable can take only ___(9)___ values.

In research studies, variables are often identified as a(n) ___(10)___ variable or a(n) ___(11)___ variable. Variables over which the investigator has control are ___(12)___ variables. The different ___(13)___ of the independent variable reflect the different ___(14)___ under study in the investigation; for example, different teaching methods. The ___(15)___ variable depends upon, or is the consequence of, the independent variable. For example, achievement in mathematics (dependent variable) ___(16)___ upon the teaching method (independent variable).

Measurement, or the assignment of ___(17)___ to characteristics according to a defined rule, is an important concept in statistics. The hierarchy of measurement scales reflects the ___(18)___ of the measurement of the dependent variable. The first level or least precise is the ___(19)___ scale. The properties of this scale are that data categories are mutually ___(20)___ and have no logical ___(21)___ . The next level in the measurement hierarchy is the ___(22)___ scale. An additional property of this scale is the ___(23)___ of the data categories. For the ordinal scale, data categories are mutually exclusive, logically ordered and ___(24)___ according to the amount of some character-

(25) interval

(26) others

(27) interval (differences)

(28) equal

(29) ratio

(30) absolute (known)

(31) measure (true point)

(32) characteristic

(33) relative

(34) population

(35) portion

(36) sample

(37) parameter

(38) statistic

(39) descriptive

(40) inferential

(41) descriptive

(42) population

(43) sample

(44) samples

(45) population

istic they possess. The next higher level of measurement is the __(25)__ scale. This scale has all the properties of the __(26)__ scales with one additional property. This property is that __(27)__ between the various levels of the categories on any part of the scale reflect __(28)__ differences in the characteristic measured. The last level or most precise scale in the measurement hierarchy is the __(29)__ scale. This scale has all the properties of the other scales and in addition has the property that zero is __(30)__ or is a __(31)__ that represents the absence of the __(32)__ measured. With this added property, statements can be made about the __(33)__ amounts of a characteristic possessed by different individuals or things.

In statistics we often talk about groups of people or things. By definition, a __(34)__ includes all members of some explicit group. A subset or a __(35)__ of a population is called a __(36)__. A characteristic of a population is defined as a __(37)__. And a characteristic of a sample is called a __(38)__.

The study of statistics is often described by two broad categories: __(39)__ statistics and __(40)__ statistics. Methods that classify and summarize numerical data are __(41)__ statistics. The use of inferential statistics allows us to make generalizations about a __(42)__ by studying a __(43)__ or subset of that population. In inferential statistics, measures are computed on sample data, and inferences are made from the __(44)__ to the __(45)__.

Comprehension Check: Answers

1. data
2. value
3. variable
4. constant
5. continuous
6. discrete
7. any
8. scale
9. designated
10. independent
11. dependent
12. independent
13. levels
14. treatments
15. dependent
16. depends
17. numbers
18. precision
19. nominal
20. exclusive
21. order
22. ordinal
23. ordering
24. scaled
25. interval
26. preceding
27. differences
28. equal
29. ratio
30. known
31. true point
32. characteristic
33. proportional
34. population
35. part
36. sample
37. parameter
38. statistic
39. descriptive
40. inferential
41. descriptive
42. population
43. sample
44. sample
45. population

Chapter 1 Exercises _ 5

1. Supply the missing words using the key words listed below.

constant	interval	ratio
continuous	nominal	sample
data	ordinal	sample mean
dependent	parameter	statistic
discrete	population	variable
independent	population mean	

(a) contents (data)
(b) constant

(c) variable

(d) independent

(e) dependent

(f) continuous

(g) discrete

(h) nominal

(i) ordinal

(j) ordinal (interval)

(k) interval (ratio)

(l) population

(m) parameter

(n) population mean

(o) sample

(p) statistic

(q) sample mean

An English teacher uses two different methods of instruction in two English classes. The effect of the different teaching methods will be determined by English achievement scores. The characteristics *English teacher* and *achievement scores* are ___(a)___ . The characteristic *English teacher* is a ___(b)___ and the characteristic *achievement scores* is a ___(c)___ . In this study, the instructional method is the ___(d)___ variable and the achievement scores are the ___(e)___ variable.

Miles per hour and miles per gallon are both examples of a ___(f)___ variable. The number of cylinders in an automobile engine is a ___(g)___ variable.

The number of males and females in a class is an example of a ___(h)___ scale of measurement. At a county fair, various kinds of home grown produce are given awards, for example, first prize, second prize, and so on. This type of measurement scale is generally considered an ___(i)___ scale. The set of scores for a class on a standardized test is an example of an ___(j)___ scale. The amount of air pressure in your car tires is measured on a ___(k)___ scale.

All third grade students in a school district would be considered a ___(l)___ . A characteristic of this group is called a ___(m)___ and would be identified using a Greek letter. The Greek letter μ is the symbol for the ___(n)___ . If we select 30 students from the school district, this subgroup would be a ___(o)___ . A characteristic of this subgroup is called a ___(p)___ and would be identified using a Latin letter. The Latin letter $\bar{X}$ is the symbol for a ___(q)___ .

(a) data
(b) variables

2. A university counseling center obtains the following information on each student that comes for help: the student's sex, age, academic department, SAT scores, and cumulative grade point average.

The information obtained about students is called ___(a)___ . The sex, age, academic department, SAT scores, and cumulative grade point average are ___(b)___ .

(c) nominal
(d) nominal (ratio)
(e) nominal
(f) ordinal (interval)
(g) ratio
(h) discrete
(i) continuous
(j) sample
(k) statistics

What is the measurement scale of the following variables?

Sex ___(c)___

Age ___(d)___

Academic department ___(e)___

SAT scores ___(f)___

Cumulative grade point average ___(g)___

Some of the variables may be called continuous or discrete. Sex and academic department are ___(h)___ variables. Age, SAT scores and cumulative grade point average are ___(i)___ variables.

Suppose that every tenth student that came into the center was selected for a study. This group would be a ___(j)___ of the students that come to the center and the characteristics of this group would be called ___(k)___ .

Chapter 1 Exercises: Answers

1. a. data
   b. constant
   c. variable
   d. independent
   e. dependent
   f. continuous
   g. discrete
   h. nominal
   i. ordinal

   j. interval
   k. ratio
   l. population
   m. parameter
   n. population mean
   o. sample
   p. statistic
   q. sample mean

2. a. data
   b. variables
   c. nominal
   d. ratio
   e. nominal
   f. interval

   g. ratio
   h. discrete
   i. continuous
   j. sample
   k. statistics

Chapter 1 Mastery Test

The director of research for a school district wants to know if there is a difference in achievement between eleventh grade and twelfth grade students taking a science course for which three different textbooks are used in three classes. The director gathers different kinds of information on two groups of 30 eleventh graders and 30 twelfth graders. This information includes each student's sex, age, class standing, SAT or pre-SAT scores, grade level, the textbook used in the class, and the final examination score.

1. What data are gathered by the director of research?
2. What characteristic is the constant in this study?
3. What are the variables in the data gathered?
4. Which variables are discrete and which are continuous?

The director has gathered data on a number of variables. Some of the variables are needed to conduct the study outlined in this exercise, and other variables could be used to conduct other studies.

5. For the study of science achievement differences for eleventh and twelfth grade students using three different textbooks what are the independent variables?
6. What is the dependent variable?
7. Of all the data gathered, which variables are measured on the following scales?
   a. Nominal
   b. Ordinal
   c. Interval
   d. Ratio

We would say that the groups of eleventh and twelfth graders are __(8)__ drawn from the __(9)__ of all eleventh and twelfth grade students in the district. The characteristics of the selected students are called __(10)__ .

Chapter 1 Mastery Test: Answers

1. sex, age, class standing, SAT or pre-SAT scores, grade level, textbook used and final examination score
2. science course
3. sex, age, class standing, SAT or pre-SAT scores, grade level, textbook used and final examination score
4. discrete: sex, class standing, grade level, textbook; continuous: age, SAT or pre-SAT scores, final examination score
5. grade level and textbook
6. final examination score
7. a. sex, textbook
   b. class standing
   c. SAT or pre-SAT scores, grade level, final examination score
   d. age
8. samples
9. population
10. statistics

Note: The classification of the variables into the categories provided in the answers may justifiably be questioned. How a variable is classified depends to some extent upon how the data are gathered and how the data are to be used. The researcher must be able to defend the choice of the measurement scale for the data being used. For comprehensive discussion of the pros and cons of relating appropriate statistical procedures to the scales of measurement interested readers are referred to the following textbook references: Anderson (1961), Kaiser (1960), Lord (1953) and Stevens (1951, 1968).

2 Organizing Data for Meaningful Representation

Comprehension Check

(1) frequency distr
(2) highest
(3) lowest
(4) rank (frequencies)
(5) range
(6) intervals
(7) class intervals
(8) distribution
(9) width
(10) uniformly
(11) midpoint
(12) manageable
(13) interpret
(14) eliminated
(15) histogram
(16) distribution polygon
(17) scores
(18) frequencies
(19) left
(20) negatively

The following summary reviews the material presented in this chapter. To check your understanding of key concepts, supply the missing words indicated by the numbered blanks.

A tabular arrangement of numbers that shows the number of times a given score or group of scores occur is a ___(1)___ . The first step in organizing data into a frequency distribution is to order scores from ___(2)___ to ___(3)___ . This step allows us to determine the ___(4)___ of individual scores and to easily identify the highest and lowest scores. Knowledge of the highest score and lowest score allows us to determine the ___(5)___ of scores. The second step is the development of a frequency distribution.

Data are often organized into classes that combine several scores into an ___(6)___ of scores. The intervals are called ___(7)___ . A frequency ___(8)___ can be constructed using class intervals. To develop frequency distributions using class intervals that have a ___(9)___ greater than one, two assumptions are necessary: first, that for any class interval, the scores are ___(10)___ distributed between the exact limits of the interval, and second, that the ___(11)___ of the class interval adequately represents the scores within the interval. While the procedure of using class intervals makes the data more ___(12)___ and easier to ___(13)___ , some specific information is ___(14)___ .

A graphic representation can help to understand the nature of data. A bar graph in which frequencies are represented by the length of the bars is called a ___(15)___ . Another graphic display is the ___(16)___ , in which scores in any class interval are represented by the midpoint of the interval. For both types of displays, ___(17)___ are plotted along the horizontal axis and ___(18)___ along the vertical axis. In either a histogram or a frequency polygon, if many frequencies are on the right-hand side of the distribution and fewer on the left-hand side, the distribution is said to be skewed to the ___(19)___ or ___(20)___ skewed. In contrast, if there are many frequencies on the left-hand side of the distribution with fewer frequencies trailing off to

(21) right
(22) positively
(23) symmetrical
(24) kurtosis
(25) platykurtic
(26) leptokurtic
(27) mesokurtic
(28) below
(29) percentage
(30) distribution (frequencies)
 location (rank)
(31)
(32) normally
(33) not
(34) ordinal
(35) cannot

the right, the distribution is said to be skewed to the ___(21)___ or ___(22)___ skewed.

A distribution is said to be ___(23)___ if the two sides would correspond exactly were the graph to be folded along a central line. Distributions may be symmetrical but vary in their degree of peakedness, a distinction called ___(24)___. A distribution with a small degree of peakedness is referred to as ___(25)___; a distribution with a high degree of peakedness is referred to as ___(26)___; and a distribution with a moderate degree of peakedness is referred to as ___(27)___.

One method used to locate a given score in a distribution of many scores is the percentile. A percentile is defined as the point in the distribution ___(28)___ which a given ___(29)___ of the scores is found. We may also calculate the percentile rank of a score in a distribution; that is, a value on the scale of ___(30)___. Percentiles can be used to indicate an individual's ___(31)___ or position within a group. However, since many variables in the behavioral sciences tend to be ___(32)___ distributed, differences between percentile points are ___(33)___ uniform throughout the scale of measurement. That is, percentiles are an example of an ___(34)___ scale of measurement, and ___(35)___ be arithmetically manipulated.

Comprehension Check: Answers

1. frequency distribution
2. highest
3. lowest
4. frequencies
5. range
6. interval
7. class intervals
8. distribution
9. width
10. uniformly
11. midpoint
12. manageable
13. interpret
14. lost
15. histogram
16. frequency polygon
17. scores
18. frequencies
19. left
20. negatively
21. right
22. positively
23. symmetric
24. kurtosis
25. platykurtic
26. leptokurtic
27. mesokurtic
28. below
29. percentage
30. percentiles
31. rank
32. normally
33. not
34. ordinal
35. cannot

Chapter 2 Exercises

1. An instructor gave a 100-point examination to a class of 25 students. The following scores resulted:

97 75 63 51 77
82 80 93 84 90
59 68 75 76 68
64 87 70 80 82
73 66 67 71 74

a. What is the range of scores?

Range $= (97 - 51) + 1$

$\quad\quad = 47$

b. Complete the following frequency distribution of examination scores.

Score	f	Score	f	Score	f
97	1	77	1	68	2
93	1	–	–	–	–
	1	–	–	–	–
	1	–	–	–	–
	2	–	–	–	–
80	–	70	–	51	–

Hint: The column labeled f is the frequency, or number of scores, for each value. The total of all the f columns will equal the total number of scores, or 25.

c. Suppose the instructor decides to combine several actual scores and form class intervals. Using the data from the frequency distribution of scores, complete the table for a frequency distribution using class intervals with a width of 5.

Class Interval	f
96–100	1
91–95	–
–	–
–	–
–	–
51–55	1

Hint: Each class interval has a width of 5 units; that is, 91 to 95 is an interval of 5. Again, the total of the f column should equal the number of scores.

1. d. Expand the frequency distribution using class intervals to include the exact limits and midpoints of the intervals.

Class Interval	Exact Limits	Midpoint	f
96–100	95.5–100.5	98	1
91–95	–	–	–
–	–	–	–
–	–	–	–
–	–	–	–
51–55	50.5–55.5	–	–

e. Using the information developed above, draw a histogram of this data. Label the horizontal and vertical axes and place values for the points on each axis.

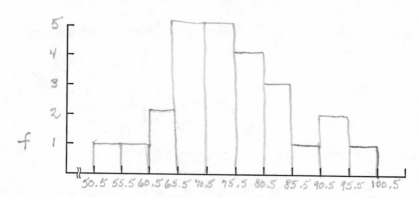

Hint: The values along the horizontal axis in a histogram are the exact limits for the class intervals, and they increase in size from left to right.

f. Draw a frequency polygon from the data in part d. Label the horizontal and vertical axes and place values for the points on each axis.

Hint: The values along the horizontal axis in a frequency polygon are the midpoints of the class intervals.

g. Compare your drawings of the histogram and the frequency polygon. Are they approximately the same in shape and location on the graphs?
Hint: The answer to this question should be yes or some error in plotting has been made. They are both graphic representations of the same frequency distribution.

h. Complete the following table using the data you developed in part d, and provide the missing information for cf, % and $c\%$.

Class Interval	Exact Limits	Midpoint	f	cf	%	$c\%$
96–100	95.5–100.5	98	1	25	4	100
91–95	–95.5	–	–	–	–	–
–	–	–	–	–	–	–
–	–	–	–	–	–	–
–	–	–	–	–	–	–
51–55	50.5–55.5	53	1	1	4	4

Hint: The cf column shows the cumulative frequency of scores in the intervals from the bottom to the top of the chart. Thus, the last, or top, interval will have a cumulative frequency equal to the total number of scores. The % column shows the percentage of the total number of scores contained in each interval. The $c\%$ column shows the cumulative percentage of scores in the intervals from the bottom to the top of the chart. Thus, the last, or top, interval will have a cumulative percentage equal to 100.

i. Suppose the instructor wants to determine the point below which 60 percent of the scores are found.

(1) The 60th percentile is in which interval? _____

(2) Using the general formula (2.2), calculate the 60th percentile. Hint: P_{60} is the point below which $.60 \times 25 = 15$ students scored. Note that the interval 70.5–75.5 has a cumulative frequency of 14 and a cumulative percentage of 56.

$$P_{60} = ll + \left(\frac{Np - cf}{f_i}\right)(i)$$

$$= \quad + \left(\frac{(25)(\quad) - }{\quad}\right)(\ )$$

$$= \quad + \left(\frac{15 - }{\quad}\right)(\ )$$

$$= \quad + \left(\frac{1}{4}\right)(\ )$$

$$= \quad +$$

$$=$$

(3) Calculate the 40th percentile.

j. One of the students in the class received a score of 82 and wants to know the relative position of this score in the distribution. In statistical terms, the student wants to know the percentile rank of the score 82.

Hint: The score 82 is in the interval 80.5–85.5, and 18 scores are below the exact lower limit of 80.5. We want to calculate the percentage of the number of scores below the score of 82.

(1) Using the general formula (2.3) calculate the percentile rank of the score 82.

$$PR_{82} = \left[\dfrac{cf + \dfrac{X - ll}{i}(f_i)}{N} \right](100)$$

$$= \left[\dfrac{+ \left(\dfrac{82 -}{5} \right)(3)}{} \right](\;\;)$$

$$= \left[\dfrac{+ \left(\dfrac{1.5}{5} \right)(3)}{25} \right](\;\;)$$

$$= \left[\dfrac{+ (\;\;)(3)}{} \right](\;\;)$$

$$= \left(\dfrac{+ 0.9}{} \right)(\;\;)$$

$$= \left(\dfrac{18.9}{25} \right)(\;\;)$$

$$= (\;\;)(\;\;)$$

$$=$$

(2) Calculate the percentile rank of the score 64.
Note: In parts i and j of this exercise the calculations have been step-by-step. Future exercises will often be presented by combining mathematical steps. Students who feel their mathematics background is weak are encouraged to consult more extensive reviews, such as Andrew R. Baggaley, *Mathematics For Introductory Statistics*, (New York: John Wiley & Sons, Inc., 1969).

k. Draw the ogive (cumulative frequency distribution) for the data developed in part h. Label the horizontal and vertical axes and place values for the points on each axis.
Compare the results of your calculations in parts i and j with what you would obtain using the ogive to determine the percentile and percentile rank.

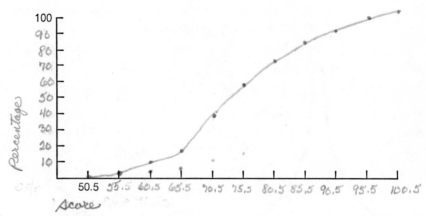

Score

Hint: The values along the horizontal axis are the exact limits of the class intervals and increase in size from left to right. Below the exact limit of the lowest class interval (50.5–55.5) no scores exist; thus, the percentage of scores below 50.5 is zero. All scores are included by the largest value of the exact limit of the highest class interval (95.5–100.5); thus the percentage of scores below 100.5 is 100.

2. Draw the frequency polygon for the following ten scores.

   1 6 3 2 3
   5 7 2 2 4

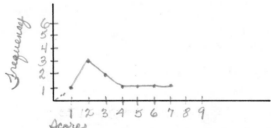

Score

3. Draw the frequency polygon for the following ten scores.

   9 8 6 7 3
   8 7 5 4 8

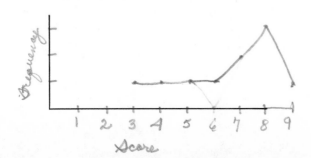

Score

4. The following are three different frequency polygons. Label the kind of distribution each represents.

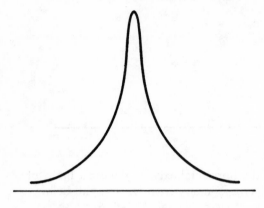

a.

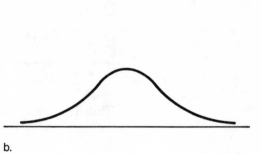

b.

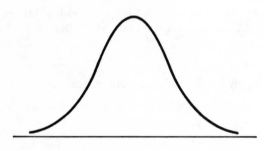

c.

Chapter 2 Exercises: Answers

1. a. Range $= (97 - 51) + 1$
$= 47$

b.

Score	f	Score	f	Score	f
97	1	77	1	68	2
93	1	76	1	67	1
90	1	75	2	66	1
87	1	74	1	64	1
84	1	73	1	63	1
82	2	71	1	59	1
80	2	70	1	51	1

c., d., and h.

Class Interval	Exact Limits	Midpoint	f	cf	%	$c\%$
96–100	95.5–100.5	98	1	25	4	100
91–95	90.5–95.5	93	1	24	4	96
86–90	85.5–90.5	88	2	23	8	92
81–85	80.5–85.5	83	3	21	12	84
76–80	75.5–80.5	78	4	18	16	72
71–75	70.5–75.5	73	5	14	20	56
66–70	65.5–70.5	68	5	9	20	36
61–65	60.5–65.5	63	2	4	8	16
56–60	55.5–60.5	58	1	2	4	8
51–55	50.5–55.5	53	1	1	4	4

e.

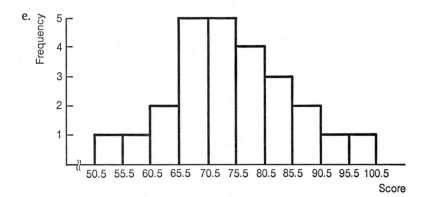

f.

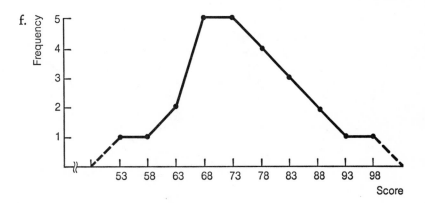

i. (1) 75.5–80.5

$$P_{60} = 75.5 + \left[\frac{(25)(.60) - 14}{4} \right] (5)$$

$$= 75.5 + \left[\frac{15 - 14}{4} \right] (5)$$

$$= 75.5 + \left(\frac{1}{4} \right) (5)$$

$$= 75.5 + 1.25$$

$$= 76.75$$

(3) $P_{40} = 71.5$

j. (1)

$$PR_{82} = \left[\frac{18 + \dfrac{82 - 80.5}{5}(3)}{25} \right] (100)$$

$$= \left[\frac{18 + (0.3)(3)}{25} \right] (100)$$

$$= \left(\frac{18.9}{25} \right) (100)$$

$$= (0.756)(100)$$

$$= 75.6$$

(2) $PR_{64} = 13.6$

k.

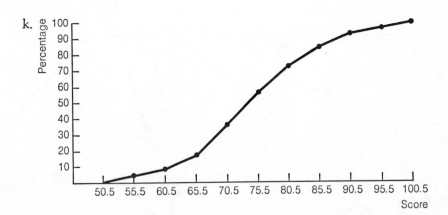

2.

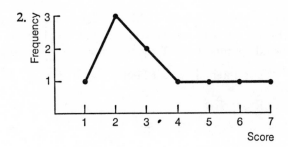

3.

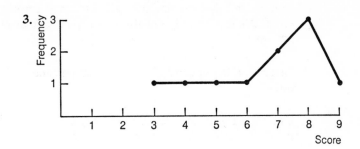

4. a. leptokurtic
   b. platykurtic
   c. mesokurtic

Chapter 2 Mastery Test

1. A traffic engineer is interested in the speed that motorists drive along a certain segment of road. A sample of vehicles was clocked to the nearest mph throughout the day, with the following results:

29	35	36	20	23
37	34	31	24	30
40	28	35	46	32
38	30	34	37	28
32	33	42	32	36
50	34	39	53	30
36	35	33	15	26
34	36	35	41	44

40
speak

   a. Develop the frequency distribution for the above data.

b. Suppose the engineer decides to develop a frequency distribution of class intervals with a width of 3. Complete the following table including cumulative frequencies and cumulative percentage.

Class Interval	Exact Limits	Midpoint	f	cf	%	$c\%$
–	–	52	–	–	–	–
–	–	–	–	–	–	–
–	–	–	–	–	–	–

c. Assume that the posted speed limit on this section of road is 35 mph and that the engineer allows 2 mph for speedometer error. What percentage of the motorists drove at or below 37 mph?

d. Determine the speed below which 85 percent of the vehicles were traveling.

e. Draw the frequency distribution and, in general terms, describe the shape of the curve.

Chapter 2 Mastery Test: Answers

1. a.

Miles per hour	f	Miles per hour	f
53	1	34	4
50	1	33	2
46	1	32	3
44	1	31	1
42	1	30	3
41	1	29	1
40	1	28	2
39	1	26	1
38	1	24	1
37	2	23	1
36	4	20	1
35	4	15	1

b.

Class Interval	Exact Limits	Midpoint	f	cf	%	$c\%$
51–53	50.5–53.5	52	1	40	2.5	100.0
48–50	47.5–50.5	49	1	39	2.5	97.5
45–47	44.5–47.5	46	1	38	2.5	95.0
42–44	41.5–44.5	43	2	37	5.0	92.5
39–41	38.5–41.5	40	3	35	7.5	87.5
36–38	35.5–38.5	37	7	32	17.5	80.0
33–35	32.5–35.5	34	10	25	25.0	62.5
30–32	29.5–32.5	31	7	15	17.5	37.5
27–29	26.5–29.5	28	3	8	7.5	20.0
24–26	23.5–26.5	25	2	5	5.0	12.5
21–23	20.5–23.5	22	1	3	2.5	7.5
18–20	17.5–20.5	19	1	2	2.5	5.0
15–17	14.5–17.5	16	1	1	2.5	2.5

c. $PR_{37} = 71.52$

d. $P_{85} = 40.5$ mph

e.

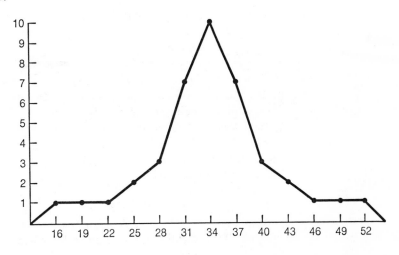

The distribution is symmetric with a moderate degree of peakedness, or mesokurtic. The shape of the distribution approximates the *normal* curve.

3 Describing Distributions: Measures of Central Tendency and Dispersion

_6

Comprehension Check

-6

The handwritten answers in the left margin:

(1) shape
(2) location
(3) dispersion
(4) polygon
(5) positively
(6) negatively
(7) leptokurtic
(8) platykurtic
(9) point (score)
(10) variability (central tendency)
(11) located
(12) mode
(13) most frequent
(14) midpoint
(15) bimodal
(16) 50th percentile
(17) below
(18) mean
(19) sum
(20) number
(21) deviations
(22) zero
(23) squares
(24) less than
(25) scale
(26) mode
(27) median
(28) mean
(29) mode
(30) median

The following summary reviews the material presented in this chapter. To check your understanding of key concepts, supply the missing words indicated by the numbered blanks.

To describe a distribution of data adequately, three kinds of information are required: knowledge of its __(1)__, __(2)__ on the measurement scale, and the __(3)__ of its scores. In discussing the shape of a distribution, we talk about the shape of the frequency __(4)__ for the scores. In Chapter 2 we indicated that a distribution may be symmetric, __(5)__ skewed, or __(6)__ skewed. It may be very peaked, __(7)__, or not peaked, __(8)__. Also, percentiles were used to locate a __(9)__ in a distribution of scores.

This chapter is concerned with measures of __(10)__ for a given set of scores and where these measures are __(11)__ on the measurement scale. The simplest index of central tendency is the __(12)__. It is defined as the __(13)__ score in a distribution and is determined by inspecting the data. The mode of a frequency distribution of class intervals is the __(14)__ of the class interval with the largest frequency. When a distribution has two modes, it is called __(15)__.

A second measure of central tendency is the median. It is defined as the __(16)__; that is, the point on the scale of measurement __(17)__ which 50 percent of the scores fall. A third measure of central tendency is the __(18)__. It is the arithmetic average of the scores in the distribution; that is, the __(19)__ of all scores divided by the __(20)__ of scores. Two properties of the mean are important. First, the sum of the __(21)__ of all scores in the distribution from the mean is __(22)__. Second, the sum of __(23)__ of deviations about the mean is __(24)__ than the sum of squares of deviations about any other value.

Which measure of central tendency is most appropriate is dependent upon the __(25)__ of measurement of the variable. The __(26)__ is appropriate for nominal data. For ordinal data, the __(27)__ and the __(28)__ are appropriate. When the data are interval or ratio, the __(29)__, __(30)__, and

(3) mean
(32) use
(33) represents
(34) sample
(35) population
(36) mean
(37) mode
(38) median
(39) mode
(40) median
(41) mean
(42) points (intervals)
(43) spread
(44) range
(45) size
(46) higher
(47) semi interquartile
(48) symmetrical
(49) less (greater)
(50) greater (less)
(51) skewness
(52) variance
(53) mean
(54) squared
(55) unbiased
(56) sample (population)
(57) squared
(58) square
(59) original or same

___(31)___ may be used. Another consideration in the choice of a measure of central tendency is the ___(32)___ to be made of the measure. If the purpose is descriptive, the measure that best ___(33)___ the data should be used. If the purpose is to infer from ___(34)___ to ___(35)___ , the ___(36)___ has the advantage, since it can be manipulated mathematically in ways not appropriate to the ___(37)___ and ___(38)___ . Neither the ___(39)___ nor the ___(40)___ is generally affected by extreme scores in a distribution. Extreme scores do affect the ___(41)___ , however.

Measures of variability are ___(42)___ on the scale of measurement that are indicators of the ___(43)___ in the distribution. The simplest measure of variation is the ___(44)___ . Its most serious limitation is that it tends to vary with the ___(45)___ of the group. Larger groups tend to have a ___(46)___ range of values than smaller groups. The limitation of the range is somewhat overcome by determining the ___(47)___ range (Q) as a measure of dispersion. If the distribution is ___(48)___ , $Q = Q_3 - \text{median} = \text{median} - Q_1$. If the distribution is positively skewed, $Q_3 - \text{median}$ will be ___(49)___ than $\text{median} - Q_1$. If the distribution is negatively skewed $Q_3 - \text{median}$ will be ___(50)___ than $\text{median} - Q_1$. Thus, the difference between $Q_1 - \text{median}$ and $\text{median} - Q_3$ is a measure of the ___(51)___ of the distribution.

The most often used measure of dispersion when the data have been measured on an interval scale is the ___(52)___ . It is defined as the ___(53)___ of the ___(54)___ deviations, that is, $\Sigma(X - \mu)^2/N$. To calculate the variance of a sample, we use $n - 1$ in the denominator of the formula to provide an ___(55)___ estimate of the ___(56)___ variance; that is, $\Sigma(X - \bar{X})^2/n - 1$. The variance is a measure of dispersion in ___(57)___ units of the measurement scale. For example, if the measurement scale were the height of people in inches, the dispersion, or variance, would be expressed in ___(58)___ inches. The square root of the variance, called the standard deviation, is the measure of dispersion in the ___(59)___ unit of measurement, linear inches.

Comprehension Check: Answers

1. shape
2. location
3. dispersion
4. polygon
5. positively
6. negatively
7. leptokurtic
8. platykurtic
9. score
10. central tendency
11. located
12. mode
13. most frequent
14. midpoint
15. bimodal
16. 50th percentile
17. below
18. mean
19. sum
20. number
21. deviations
22. zero
23. squares
24. smaller
25. scale
26. mode
27. median
28. mode
29. mean
30. median
31. mode
32. use
33. describes
34. samples
35. populations
36. mean
37. median
38. mode
39. mode

40. median
41. mean
42. intervals
43. dispersion
44. range
45. size
46. larger
47. semi-interquartile
48. symmetrical
49. greater
50. less
51. skewness
52. variance
53. mean
54. squared
55. unbiased
56. population
57. squared
58. square
59. original

Chapter 3 Exercises

1. A class of 20 students has the following final examination scores.

90 75 91 76 72
72 87 64 75 80
68 83 79 72 88
95 70 73 81 74

a. Develop the frequency distribution.

Score f cf

b. What is the mode of this distribution of scores?

c. What is the median of this distribution of scores?

$$\text{Mdn} = ll + \left[\frac{N(0.50) - cf}{f_i}\right](i)$$

$$= 74.5 + \left[\frac{(0.50) - 8}{2}\right](1)$$

$$= \qquad +$$

$$=$$

d. What is the mean of this distribution of scores?

$$\mu = \frac{\Sigma X}{N}$$

$$= \frac{\quad}{\quad}$$

$$=$$

2. a. What is the mode of the following distribution of scores?

Class Interval	Exact Limits	Midpoint	f	cf
70–74	69.5–74.5	72	8	110
65–69	–	67	12	102
60–64	–	62	10	90
55–59	–	57	16	80
50–54	–	52	24	64
45–49	–	47	18	40
40–44	–	42	15	22
35–39	34.5–39.5	37	7	7

b. What is the median of this distribution of scores?

$$Mdn = \quad + \left[\frac{110(\quad) - }{\quad} \right]( )$$

$$= \quad +$$

$$=$$

3. What is the range of scores in exercise 1?

$$Range = (\quad - \quad) + 1$$

$$= \quad +$$

$$=$$

4. a. What is the semi-interquartile range for the scores in exercise 2?

$$Q = \frac{Q_3 - Q_1}{2} \qquad Q_3 = P_{75} = 59.5 + \left[\frac{110(\quad) - }{\quad} \right]( )$$

$$= \quad +$$

$$=$$

$$Q_1 = P_{25} = \quad + \left[\frac{(.25) - }{18} \right]( )$$

$$= \quad +$$

$$=$$

$$= \frac{\quad - \quad}{2}$$

$$=$$

b. Is the distribution positively skewed or negatively skewed?

$$Q_3 - Mdn = \qquad - \qquad =$$

$$Mdn - Q_1 = \qquad - \qquad =$$

5. a. In a swimming event, eight swimmers had the following times in seconds. Consider this group of swimmers to be a population. What is the variance in their scores using the deviation formula?

Time	$(X - \mu)$	$(X - \mu)^2$
28	−5	25
29	+4	16
29	−4	16
32	−1	1
32	−1	1
36	+3	9
38	+5	25
40	7	49
$\Sigma = 264$	0	142

$\mu = 33$

$$\sigma^2 = \frac{\Sigma(X - \mu)^2}{N}$$

$$= \underline{}$$

$$= 17.75$$

Hint: The sum of $X - \mu$ is zero.

b. Considering this group of swimmers to be a sample, what is the variance in their scores?

$$s^2 = \frac{\Sigma(X - \bar{X})^2}{n - 1}$$

$$= \underline{}$$

$$=$$

c. What is the unit of measurement for the variance in parts a and b?

6. a. The times from exercise 5 are reproduced below. Assume this group of swimmers to be a population. What is the variance in their scores using the raw score formula?

Time	X^2
28	784
29	841
29	– 841
32	– 1024
32	– 1024
36	– 1296
38	– 1444
40	– 1600

$$\Sigma = 264$$

$$\sigma^2 = \frac{\Sigma X^2 - \frac{(\Sigma X)^2}{N}}{N}$$

$$= \frac{8854 - \frac{(264)^2}{8}}{8}$$

$$= \frac{8854 - 8712}{8}$$

$$= 17.75$$

Hint: Be careful of the difference between ΣX^2 and $(\Sigma X)^2$.

b. Assume the same group of swimmers to be a sample. What is the variance in their scores using the raw score formula?

$$s^2 = \frac{\Sigma X^2 - \frac{(\Sigma X)^2}{n}}{n - 1}$$

$$= \frac{8854 - \frac{(264)^2}{8}}{8 - 1}$$

$$= \frac{8854 - 8712}{7}$$

$$= 20.29$$

7. a. What is the standard deviation of scores for the population of swimmers in exercise 6a?

$$\sigma = \sqrt{\sigma^2} \text{ or } \sigma = \sqrt{\frac{\Sigma(X - \mu)^2}{N}}$$

$$= \sqrt{}$$

$$= 4.21$$

b. What is the standard deviation of scores for the sample group of swimmers in exercise 6b?

$$s = \sqrt{s^2} \text{ or } s = \sqrt{\frac{\Sigma(X - \bar{X})^2}{n - 1}}$$

$$= \sqrt{\rule{2cm}{0pt}}$$

$$=$$

8. a. Members of a gymnastics class, when attempting to complete a routine within a specified time limit, required 5, 6, 11, 9, 5, 7, 3, 4, 10, 8, 12, and 7 trials. What are the mean, median and mode for this distribution?

b. Using the deviation formula, find the variance and standard deviation. Assume the class to be a population.

X	$X - \mu$	$(X - \mu)^2$
5	$^-2.25$	$-$
6	$^-1.25$	$-$
11	$- +3.75$	$-$
9	$- +1.75$	$-$
5	$- -2.25$	$-$
7	$- -0.25$	$-$
3	$- -4.25$	$-$
4	$- -3.25$	$-$
10	$- +2.75$	$-$
8	$-+0.75$	$-$
12	$- +4.75$	$-$
7	$- -0.25$	$-$
	0	

$$\sigma^2 = \frac{\Sigma(X-\mu)^2}{N} = \frac{88.25}{12}$$

$$= 7.35$$

$$\sigma = 2.71$$

c. Using the raw score formula, find the variance and standard deviation. Assume the gymnastics class to be a sample.

$$n =$$
$$\Sigma X =$$
$$\Sigma X^2 =$$

$$s^2 = \frac{\Sigma X^2 - \frac{(\Sigma X)^2}{n}}{n - 1}$$

$$= \frac{719 - \frac{(87)^2}{12}}{12 - 1}$$

$$= \frac{719 - 630.75}{11} = 8.02$$

$$s = 2.83$$

Chapter 3 Exercises: Answers

1. a.

Score	f	cf
95	1	20
91	1	19
90	1	18
88	1	17
87	1	16
83	1	15
81	1	14
80	1	13
79	1	12
76	1	11
75	2	10
74	1	8
73	1	7
72	3	6
70	1	3
68	1	2
64	1	1

b. Mode $= 72$

c. $\text{Mdn} = 74.5 + \left[\frac{20(0.50) - 8}{2} \right] (1)$

$$= 74.5 + 1$$

$$= 75.5$$

d. $\mu = \frac{1565}{20}$

$$= 78.25$$

2. a.

Class Interval	Exact Limits	Midpoint	f	cf
70–74	69.5–74.5	72	8	110
65–69	64.5–69.5	67	12	102
60–64	59.5–64.5	62	10	90
55–59	54.5–59.5	57	16	80
50–54	49.5–54.5	52	24	64
45–49	44.5–49.5	47	18	40
40–44	39.5–44.5	42	15	22
35–39	34.5–39.5	37	7	7

Mode = 52

b. $\text{Mdn} = 49.5 + \left[\dfrac{110(0.50) - 40}{24} \right](5)$

$= 49.5 + \dfrac{15}{24}(5)$

$= 52.625$

3. $\text{Range} = (95 - 64) + 1$

$= 31 + 1$

$= 32$

4. a. $Q = \dfrac{Q_3 - Q_1}{2}$ $Q_3 = P_{75} = 59.5 + \left[\dfrac{110(0.75) - 80}{10} \right](5)$

$= 59.5 + 1.25$

$= 60.75$

$Q_1 = P_{25} = 44.5 + \left[\dfrac{110(0.25) - 22}{18} \right](5)$

$= 44.5 + 1.53$

$= 46.03$

$= \dfrac{60.75 - 46.03}{2}$

$= 7.36$

b. $Q_3 - \text{Mdn} = 60.75 - 52.625 = 8.125$
$\text{Mdn} - Q_1 = 52.625 - 46.03 = 6.595$
Positively skewed

5. a.

Time	$(X - \mu)$	$(X - \mu)^2$
28	-5	25
29	-4	16
29	-4	16
32	-1	1
32	-1	1
36	3	9
38	5	25
40	7	49
$\Sigma = 264$	0	142

$$\mu = 33.0$$

$$\sigma^2 = \frac{142}{8}$$

$$= 17.75$$

b. $s^2 = \dfrac{142}{7}$

$$= 20.29$$

c. square seconds

6. a.

Time	X^2
28	784
29	841
29	841
32	1024
32	1024
36	1296
38	1444
40	1600
$\Sigma = 264$	8854

$$\sigma^2 = \frac{8854 - \dfrac{(264)^2}{8}}{8}$$

$$= \frac{8854 - 8712}{8}$$

$$= 17.75$$

b. $s^2 = \dfrac{8854 - \dfrac{(264)^2}{8}}{8 - 1}$

$= \dfrac{8854 - 8712}{7}$

$= 20.29$

Note: Notice that you get the same answers whether you use the deviation formula or the raw score formula. However, the deviation formula requires that you determine μ or $\overline{X}$ and $(X - \mu)^2$ or $(X - \overline{X})^2$. This can be troublesome if μ or $\overline{X}$ is a fraction. Therefore, the raw score formula is more efficient and easier to compute, even though large numbers must be handled sometimes.

7. a. $\sigma = \sqrt{17.75}$
   $= 4.21$

   b. $s = \sqrt{20.29}$
   $= 4.50$

8. a. Mode $= 5$ and 7 (bimodal)

   Median $= 6.5 + \left[\dfrac{12(0.5) - 5}{2} \right] (1)$

   $= 6.5 + (0.5)(1)$

   $= 7$

   Mean $= \dfrac{87}{12} = 7.25$

   b.

X	$X - \mu$	$(X - \mu)^2$
5	-2.25	5.06
6	-1.25	1.56
11	3.75	14.06
9	1.75	3.06
5	-2.25	5.06
7	-0.25	0.06
3	-4.25	18.06
4	-3.25	10.56
10	2.75	7.56
8	0.75	0.56
12	4.75	22.56
7	-0.25	0.06
	0.00	88.22

$$\sigma^2 = \frac{88.22}{12}$$

$$= 7.35$$

$$\sigma = 2.71$$

c. $n = 12$
$\Sigma X = 87$
$\Sigma X^2 = 719$

$$s^2 = \frac{719 - \dfrac{(87)^2}{12}}{12 - 1}$$

$$= \frac{719 - 630.75}{11}$$

$$= 8.02$$

$$s = 2.83$$

Chapter 3 Mastery Test

1. The mean of a set of six scores is 23. The first five scores are 18, 35, 26, 24, and 15. What is the sixth score?

2. Which of the three measures of central tendency lends itself most readily to mathematical manipulation?

3. For the following set of scores show that the sum of squares of deviations about the mean ($\mu = 5$) is smaller than the sum of squares of deviations about the value $\bar{X} = 6$.

$\mu = 5$

X_i	$(X_i - \mu)$	$(X_i - \mu)^2$	$(X_i - 6)$	$(X_i - 6)^2$
4	- -1	- 1	- -2	- 4
7	- +2	- 4	- +1	- 1
3	- -2	- 4	- -3	- 9
8	- +3	- 9	- +2	- 4
4	- -1	- 1	- -2	- 4
6	- +1	- 1	- 0	- 0
3	- -2	- 4	- -3	- 9
5	- 0	- 0	- -1	- 1
	0	(24)	<	(32)

4. Computation of a variance or standard deviation requires that the data be measured on at least what scale?

5. Computation of a range or semi-interquartile range requires that the data be measured on at least what scale?

6. What three types of information are needed to describe a distribution adequately?

7. What is meant by the term unbiased estimate?

8. Locate the mean, median and mode on each of the following distributions.

a.

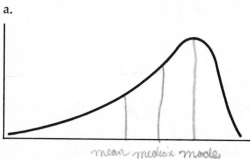

mean median mode

b.

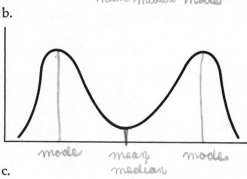

mode   mean   mode
                median

c.

mean
median
mode

X f cf
209 1 7
198 2 6
187 1 4
176 1
165 1 2
154 1 1

$mdn = ll + \left(\dfrac{N(.5)-cf}{fi}\right)$

$186.5 + 3.5 =$

$\sigma^2 = \dfrac{\Sigma(X-\mu)^2}{N}$
$=$

9. A group of weight lifters, after three attempts, lifted the following maximum weights in pounds. The data are considered a population.

165   198   209   187   176   198   154

a. What are the mode, median and mean for this distribution?

b. What are the variance and standard deviation of the population distribution?

632.02
199.94
199.94
9.86
61.78
355.70
891.62

Chapter 3 Mastery Test: Answers

1. $\displaystyle\sum_{i=1}^{6} X = (23)(6) = 138$

$\displaystyle\sum_{i=1}^{5} X = 18 + 35 + 26 + 24 + 15 = 118;$ therefore, $X_6 = 20$

2. the mean

3.

X_i	$(X_i - \mu)$	$(X_i - \mu)^2$	$(X_i - 6)$	$(X_i - 6)^2$
4	−1	1	−2	4
7	2	4	1	1
3	−2	4	−3	9
8	3	9	2	4
4	−1	1	−2	4
6	1	1	0	0
3	−2	4	−3	9
5	0	0	−1	1
		$\Sigma = 24$		$\Sigma = 32$

4. interval scale

5. ordinal scale

6. information regarding the shape, the location on the measurement scale, and the dispersion of scores

7. An estimate is unbiased if the mean of all possible values of the estimate for a given sample size equals the parameter being estimated.

8. a.

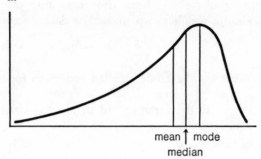

b.

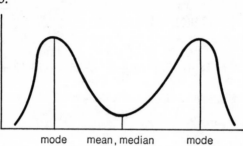

c.

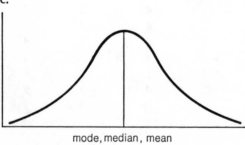

9. a. 198, 187, 183.86

   b. $\sigma^2 = 335.84$, $\sigma = 18.33$

4 Standard Scores and the Normal Curve

Comprehension Check

The following summary reviews the material presented in this chapter. To check your understanding of key concepts, supply the missing words indicated by the numbered blanks.

Raw scores and percentile ranks are for the most part ___(1)___ for making comparisons across distributions. One way that comparisons of scores can be made meaningful is through the use of ___(2)___ scores. The standard score, or ___(3)___, indicates the number of ___(4)___ deviations that a corresponding raw score is above or below the ___(5)___. A negative z-score indicates that the raw score is ___(6)___ the mean; a positive z-score indicates that the raw score is ___(7)___ the mean. A raw score that is equal to the mean has a standard score of ___(8)___. If each raw score in a distribution is converted to a z-score, the original distribution of scores is transformed into a distribution that has an identical ___(9)___, but with a mean equal to ___(10)___ and standard deviation equal to ___(11)___.

There are some undesirable characteristics of z-scores. To report z-scores to two decimal places implies a precision that ___(12)___ scores clearly do not possess. Overlooking a minus sign for a z-score can drastically change the ___(13)___ of the score. To overcome these undesirable characteristics, z-scores can be transformed to a distribution of scores with a ___(14)___ of 50 and ___(15)___ of 10, called a ___(16)___. Therefore, a transformed distribution is obtained by converting raw scores to ___(17)___, which are then transformed into a distribution with the desired ___(18)___ and ___(19)___.

Suppose an individual wishes to combine a number of scores from several tests into a total score and to weight the scores differently. The appropriate procedure would be to compute the ___(20)___ average for each score. In this procedure, each of the raw scores is first converted to a ___(21)___ and weighted appropriately. This composite score is also expressed as a standard score and can be ___(22)___ into another transformed distribution, such as a *T-distribution*.

(23) normal curve
(24) family
(25) mean
(26) standard dev.
(27) mesokurtic (symmetrical)
(28) mean
(29) asymptotic
(30) unit normal
(31) mean
(32) standard dev.
(33) number (proportion)
(34) standard normal

When we say that many physical and psychological traits are normally distributed, we are referring to a *bell-shaped* frequency polygon, or the __(23)__ . The normal curve is not a single curve but a __(24)__ of curves, each of which is determined by its __(25)__ and __(26)__ . These curves have similar properties. The unimodal, __(27)__ , and "bell shaped" curves each have a maximum height at the __(28)__ . Also, the normal curve is continuous and is __(29)__ to the *X*-axis, when graphed.

In order to work effectively with a variety of normal distributions with different means and standard deviations, a standardized normal distribution has been developed. The standard normal distribution or __(30)__ distribution is the distribution of normally distributed standard scores with a __(31)__ equal to zero and a __(32)__ equal to one. Using the properties of the unit normal curve, we can determine the __(33)__ of scores that are between two given values of the distribution. Percentiles and percentile ranks can be calculated using the __(34)__ curve.

Comprehension Check: Answers

1. inappropriate
2. standard
3. z-score
4. standard
5. mean
6. below
7. above
8. zero
9. shape
10. zero
11. one
12. raw
13. meaning
14. mean
15. standard deviation
16. *T*-distribution
17. z-scores
18. mean
19. standard deviation
20. weighted
21. z-score
22. transformed
23. normal curve
24. family
25. mean
26. standard deviation
27. symmetrical
28. mean
29. asymptotic
30. unit normal
31. mean
32. standard deviation
33. proportion
34. standard normal

Chapter 4 Exercises

1. A distribution of scores has a mean of 73 and a standard deviation of 11. What are the standard scores for the following raw scores: 80, 69, 61, and 96?

$$z = \frac{X - \mu}{\sigma}$$

$$z_{80} = \frac{80 - }{11} = 0.64$$

$$z_{69} = \frac{- 73}{} = -$$

$$z_{61} = \frac{-}{} =$$

$$z_{96} = \frac{-}{} =$$

2. Suppose a teacher wanted to transform the raw scores in exercise 1 to T-scores. What are the T-scores?

$$T = 10(z) + 50$$

Raw score	z-score	T-score
80	0.64	$10(0.64) + 50 = 56.4$
69	-	$10(\quad) + 50 =$
61	-	$(\quad) + \quad =$
96	-	$(\quad) + \quad =$

3. Assume the teacher in exercise 2 decides that the distribution of scores would be more useful if the scores had a mean of 100 and a standard deviation of 15. What would be the new scores for the following raw scores?

$$X' = (\sigma')(z) + \mu'$$

Raw score	z-score	New score
85	1.09	116.35
73	-	-
60	-	-
91	-	-

4. The mean final examination scores for all eleventh grade English students in a school district is 81 and the variance is 36 (standard deviation is 6). What are the standard scores for the raw scores of 90, 80, 70, and 60?

a. $z_{90} = \dfrac{-}{} =$

b. $z_{80} =$

c. $z_{70} =$

d. $z_{60} =$

5. Transform the raw scores in exercise 4 to T-scores.

a. $10(\quad) + \quad =$

b.

c.

d.

6. A teacher wants to compare the four scores in exercise 4 with the same students' scores in another distribution that has a mean of 71 and a standard deviation of 8.5. The raw scores are 95, 92, 88, and 77. What are the values of comparable scores in the second distribution?

7. The following scores were achieved by the ten members of a mathematics class on a comprehensive final examination. Compute the corresponding z-scores.

$a_x = 12.33$
$a_y = 9.80$

$p_x = 174$

$p_y = 78$

$z = \dfrac{X - p}{\sigma_x}$

Theory (X)	Computation (Y)	$X - \mu_x$	$Y - \mu_y$	z_x	z_y
81	88	7	10	0.57	1.02
60	75	−14	−3	−1.14	−0.31
90	85	−16	−7	1.30	−0.71
75	78	−1	−0	0.08	0
95	98	21	20	1.70	2.04
55	69	−19	−9	−1.54	−0.92
70	68	−4	−10	−0.32	−1.02
82	82	8	4	0.65	0.41
64	72	−10	−6	−0.81	−0.61
68	65	−6	−13	−0.49	−1.33

$$\mu_x = \frac{\Sigma X}{N} = \frac{}{} =$$

$$\mu_y = \frac{\Sigma Y}{N} = \frac{}{} =$$

$$\sigma_x = \sqrt{\frac{\Sigma(X - \mu_x)^2}{N}} = \sqrt{\frac{}{}} =$$

$$\sigma_y = \sqrt{\frac{\Sigma(Y - \mu_y)^2}{N}} = \sqrt{\frac{}{}} =$$

Hint: $z_x = \dfrac{X - \mu_x}{\sigma_x}$ and $z_y = \dfrac{Y - \mu_y}{\sigma_y}$

8. In exercise 7 the instructor wants to weight the mathematics computation portion of the final examination twice as heavily as the theory portion in order to arrive at a combined score. What are the combined z-scores for the first four students?

z_x	z_y	Combined Score

$$\frac{\Sigma Wz}{\Sigma W} = \frac{1(z_x) + 2(z_y)}{1+2}$$

0.57	1.02	$\dfrac{1(0.57) + 2(\quad)}{3} =$
-1.14	-0.31	$\dfrac{1(\quad) + 2(-0.31)}{\quad} = -0.59$
1.30	0.71	$\underline{\hspace{3cm}} =$
0.08	0.00	$\underline{\hspace{3cm}} =$

9. What is the height (ordinate) of the standard normal curve for the following standard scores?

Standard score	Ordinate
$+1.00$	0.2420
$+1.35$	–
-0.54	–
-1.83	–

10. What is the area under the standard normal curve for the following z-scores?

z-score	Area
0.00 to $+0.75$	0.2734
0.00 to -0.37	–
-0.67 to $+1.25$	–
$+0.35$ to $+1.67$	–

Hint: It may be helpful to draw the normal curve and identify the areas. For z-score values that span 0, remember to add both the plus and minus areas for the total area.

11. Assume that the mean of a distribution of 8,500 scores is 102 and the standard deviation is 18. What score would a student have to receive so that 90 percent of the scores are lower?

$$X' = (\sigma')(z) + \mu'$$
$$= (18)(\quad) +$$
$$= \quad +$$
$$=$$

Hint: The z in the formula needs to be determined from the area under the standard normal curve that contains 90 percent of the area.

12. What would be the percentile rank of a score of 90 in the distribution of exercise 11?

$$z = \dfrac{-}{\quad} =$$

Percentile rank of the score 90 is _____.
Hint: The area between $z = -0.67$ and $z = 0$ is 0.2486.

Chapter 4 Exercises: Answers

1. $z_{80} = \dfrac{80 - 73}{11} = 0.64$

   $z_{69} = \dfrac{69 - 73}{11} = -0.36$

   $z_{61} = \dfrac{61 - 73}{11} = -1.09$

   $z_{96} = \dfrac{96 - 73}{11} = 2.09$

2.
Raw score	z-score	T-score
80	0.64	$56.4 = 10(0.64) + 50$
69	-0.36	$46.4 = 10(-0.36) + 50$
61	-1.09	$39.1 = 10(-1.09) + 50$
96	2.09	$70.9 = 10(2.09) + 50$

3.
Raw score	z-score	New score
85	1.09	$116.35 = 15(1.09) + 100$
73	0	$100.0 = 15(0) + 100$
60	-1.18	$82.30 = 15(-1.18) + 100$
91	1.64	$124.60 = 15(1.64) + 100$

4. a. $z_{90} = \dfrac{90 - 81}{6} = 1.5$

b. $z_{80} = \dfrac{80 - 81}{6} = -0.17$

c. $z_{70} = \dfrac{70 - 81}{6} = -1.83$

d. $z_{60} = \dfrac{60 - 81}{6} = -3.5$

5. a. $10(1.5) + 50 = 65.0$

b. $10(-0.17) + 50 = 48.3$

c. $10(-1.83) + 50 = 31.7$

d. $10(-3.5) + 50 = 15.0$

6.

Raw score	z-score	New score
95	2.33	90.81
92	1.83	86.56
88	1.16	80.49
77	-0.67	65.31

7.

Theory (X)	Computation (Y)	$X - \mu_x$	$Y - \mu_y$	z_x	z_y
81	88	7	10	0.57	1.02
60	75	-14	-3	-1.14	-0.31
90	85	16	7	1.30	0.71
75	78	1	0	0.08	0.00
95	98	21	20	1.70	2.04
55	69	-19	-9	-1.54	-0.92
70	68	-4	-10	-0.32	-1.02
82	82	8	4	0.65	0.41
64	72	-10	-6	-0.81	-0.61
68	65	-6	-13	-0.49	-1.33

$\mu_x = \dfrac{740}{10} = 74.0$

$\mu_y = \dfrac{780}{10} = 78.0$

$\sigma_x = \sqrt{\dfrac{1520}{10}} = 12.33$

$\sigma_y = \sqrt{\dfrac{960}{10}} = 9.80$

8.

z_x	z_y	Combined Score
0.57	1.02	$\dfrac{1(0.57) + 2(1.02)}{3} = 0.87$
-1.14	-0.31	$\dfrac{1(-1.14) + 2(-0.31)}{3} = -0.59$
1.30	0.71	$\dfrac{1(1.30) + 2(0.71)}{3} = 0.91$
0.08	0.00	$\dfrac{1(0.08) + 2(0.00)}{3} = 0.03$

9.

Standard score	Ordinate
$+1.00$	0.2420
$+1.35$	0.1604
-0.54	0.3448
-1.83	0.0748

10.

z-score	Area
0.00 to $+0.75$	0.2734
0.00 to -0.37	0.1443
-0.67 to $+1.25$	0.6430 (0.2486 + 0.3944)
$+0.35$ to $+1.67$	0.3157 (0.4525 − 0.1368)

11. $X' = (18)(1.282) + 102$
$= 23.076 + 102$
$= 125.076$ or 125

12. $z = \dfrac{90 - 102}{18} = -0.67$

The area beyond $z = -0.67$ is $0.5000 - 0.2486$, or 0.2514.
Percentile rank of the score 90 is 25.14, or 25.

Chapter 4 Mastery Test

1. a. Applicants for an occupational training program were
administered a test designed to provide a measure of eye-hand
coordination. The group mean was 65, with a standard deviation
of 8. The scores were normally distributed. What z-scores
correspond to raw scores of 49, 55, 65, and 72?

b. What raw scores were obtained by applicants with z-scores of 2.0, −1.0, −0.25, and 1.50?

c. What percentage of scores is above 75?

d. What percentage of scores is between 43 and 73?

e. What is the 67th percentile?

f. What is the percentile rank of a score of 51?

g. T-scores of 40, 65, 75, and 80 correspond to what raw scores?

2. a. A student's z-scores on three separate tests are 1.78, 2.68, and 1.93. What is the student's combined z-score if all tests are counted equally?

b. What is the student's combined z-score if the latter two tests are each considered twice as important as the first?

3. A student's final scores in mathematics and English are 83 and 86, respectively. Assume that the class averages are 84 and 88, with standard deviations of 5.3 and 7.2. Which is the better of the student's two scores?

4. What is the major reason that percentile ranks are inappropriate for making comparisons across distributions?

5. What are the values of the mean and standard deviation of any distribution of standard scores?

6. Is it true or false that a standard score is negative if and only if the corresponding raw score falls below the mean?

7. Find the ordinate of the standard normal curve for each of the following z-scores.

a. $z = 1.50$

b. $z = -2.33$

c. $z = 0.25$

8. Find the area under the standard normal curve for each of the following intervals.

   a. between $z = 1.00$ and $z = 2.00$

   b. above $z = 2.10$

   c. below $z = 1.75$

   d. between $z = -1.25$ and $z = 1.25$

   e. above $z = -2.46$

   f. below $z = -0.82$

9. The 500 members of the freshman class at College C have completed an English placement examination. Assume the scores to be normally distributed, with a mean of 72 and standard deviation of 10, and determine each of the following.

   a. The number of students who achieved a score of 88 or above.

   b. The number of students who scored less than 60.

   c. The 75th percentile.

   d. The 30th percentile.

   e. The percentile rank of a score of 75.

   f. The percentile rank of a score of 65.

10. The mean of a T-distribution is ___(a)___ and the standard deviation is ___(b)___ .

Chapter 4 Mastery Test: Answers

1. a. $z_{49} = \dfrac{49 - 65}{8} = -2.00$ $z_{55} = \dfrac{55 - 65}{8} = -1.25$

   $z_{65} = \dfrac{65 - 65}{8} = 0.00$ $z_{72} = \dfrac{72 - 65}{8} = 0.875$

   b. $2.0 = \dfrac{X_1 - 65}{8}$ $X_1 = 81$

$$-1.0 = \frac{X_2 - 65}{8} \qquad X_2 = 57$$

$$-0.25 = \frac{X_3 - 65}{8} \qquad X_3 = 63$$

$$1.50 = \frac{X_4 - 65}{8} \qquad X_4 = 77$$

c. $z_{75} = \dfrac{75 - 65}{8} = 1.25$

10.56%

d. $z_{43} = \dfrac{43 - 65}{8} = -2.75$

$z_{73} = \dfrac{73 - 65}{8} = 1.00$

49.70% + 34.13% = 83.83%

e. 67 percent of the scores were below $z = 0.44$ .1056

$0.44 = \dfrac{X - 65}{8}$

$X = 68.552$

$P_{67} = 69$

f. $z_{51} = \dfrac{51 - 65}{8} = -1.75$

$PR_{51} = 4.01$

g.
$40 = 10(z) + 50$	$65 = 10(z) + 50$
$z = -1.00$	$z = 1.50$
raw score = 57	raw score = 77
$75 = 10(z) + 50$	$80 = 10(z) + 50$
$z = 2.50$	$z = 3.00$
raw score = 85	raw score = 89

2. a. Combined score $= \dfrac{1.78 + 2.68 + 1.93}{3} = 2.13$

b. Combined score $= \dfrac{1.78 + 2(2.68) + 2(1.93)}{5} = 2.20$

3. $z_{83} = \dfrac{83 - 84}{5.3} = -0.19$

$z_{86} = \dfrac{86 - 88}{7.2} = -0.28$

The mathematics score is the better of the two scores.

4. Percentiles form only an ordinal scale; the size of difference in raw score units for a given difference in percentile ranks is not the same at different points in the distribution.

5. Mean = 0
Standard deviation = 1

6. true

7. a. 0.1295

   b. 0.0264

   c. 0.3867

8. a. 0.1359   d. 0.7888

   b. 0.0179   e. 0.9931

   c. 0.9599   f. 0.2061

9. a. $z_{88} = 1.60$ $0.0548(500) = 27$

   b. $z_{60} = -1.20$ $0.1151(500) = 58$

   c. 75 percent of scores were below $z = 0.675$
   $$0.675 = \dfrac{X - 72}{10}$$
   $X = 78.75$
   $P_{75} = 79$

   d. $P_{30} = 67$ e. $PR_{75} = 62$ f. $PR_{65} = 24$

10. a. 50   b. 10

5 Correlation: The Measure of Relationship

Comprehension Check

The following summary reviews the material presented in this chapter. To check your understanding of key concepts, supply the missing words indicated by the numbered blanks.

The Pearson product–moment correlation coefficient (r) is defined as the measure or the index of the relationship between two variables. The values that r can take range from ___(1)___ inclusive. The plus or minus sign indicates the ___(2)___ of the relationship or the direction of the ___(3)___ of the scattergram of data points for the variables. A positive correlation coefficient indicates a tendency of low scores on one variable to be associated with ___(4)___ scores on the second variable and high scores on the first variable to be associated with ___(5)___ scores on the second variable. On the other hand, a minus or ___(6)___ correlation indicates a tendency of low scores on one variable to be associated with ___(7)___ scores on the second variable and high scores on the first variable to be associated with ___(8)___ scores on the second variable.

The absolute value of the correlation coefficient indicates the ___(9)___ of the relationship between the two variables. As a rule of thumb, .00 to .30 (or .00 to −.30) indicates little if any correlation; .30 to .50 (or −.30 to −.50) ___(10)___ positive (or negative) correlation; .50 to .70 (or −.50 to −.70) ___(11)___ positive (or negative) correlation, .70 to .90 (or −.70 to −.90) high ___(12)___ (or negative) correlation; and .90 to 1.00 (or −.90 to −1.00) ___(13)___ (or negative) correlation.

The basic assumption underlying use of the Pearson r is that the two variables being correlated have a ___(14)___ relationship. That is, the data points on a scattergram tend to locate along a ___(15)___. This is not to say that all points must fall exactly along a straight line, but that the points display a ___(16)___ scatter about a straight line.

There are, however, variables in behavioral science research that have a ___(17)___ relationship. If the Pearson r were calculated for curvilinear data, the resulting coefficient would reflect an ___(18)___ of the actual relationship

(19) inappropriate
(20) homogeneity
(21) size
(22) lower (small)
(23) is reduced to
(24) homogeneous
(25) lower (smaller)
(26) relationship
(27) caused
(28) consideration
(29) determination
(30) variance
physical strength
(31)
(32) variance

between the two variables. Thus the Pearson r is ___(19)___ for curvilinear data.

The ___(20)___ of the data for the groups being correlated also affects the ___(21)___ of the Pearson r. If the group is homogeneous (meaning there is a restricted range of scores on either or both variables), the variance in the scores is ___(22)___. As the variance tends toward zero, the variable ___(23)___ to a constant and if either or both variables become constant, the formula for r becomes meaningless. Thus, when the group is ___(24)___, the resulting correlation coefficient will be ___(25)___ than one resulting from heterogeneous groups.

Although the correlation coefficient is an index of the ___(26)___ between two variables, it does not necessarily follow that scores on one variable are ___(27)___ by scores on the second variable. A third variable or a combination of other variables may cause the correlated relationship. Causation can be established only after careful ___(28)___ of the variables in the specific context of the investigation.

An appropriate interpretation of r may be made in terms of variance. The square of the correlation coefficient (r^2) is called the coefficient of ___(29)___ and is defined as the proportion of variance in one variable that can be associated with the ___(30)___ in the other variable. For example, suppose the correlation between age and physical strength for a group of individuals is .50. Squaring r, we find $.50^2 = 0.25$, and we can conclude that for this sample 25 percent of the variance in ___(31)___ is associated with the age of the individuals. The remaining 75 percent of the ___(32)___ not associated with age may be attributed to other factors, such as the individuals' health, physical conditioning, motivation, and so on.

Comprehension Check: Answers

1. +1.0 to −1.0
2. direction
3. slope
4. low
5. high
6. negative
7. high
8. low
9. magnitude
10. low
11. moderate
12. positive
13. very high positive
14. linear
15. straight line
16. random
17. curvilinear
18. underestimate
19. inappropriate
20. homogeneity
21. size
22. small
23. reduces
24. homogeneous
25. smaller
26. relationship
27. caused
28. consideration
29. determination
30. variance
31. physical strength
32. variance

Chapter 5 Exercises

1. The following data are the English aptitude scores (X) and English grades earned (Y) for 10 students. Using the deviation formula (5.2) calculate the correlation coefficient.

X	Y	$x = (X - \bar{X})$	$y = (Y - \bar{Y})$	xy	x^2	y^2
580	85	77	10	770	5,929	100
520	85	17	10	170	289	100
470	70	-33	-5	-165	-	-
465	60	-38	-15	-570	-	-
500	80	-3	5	-15	-	-
510	65	7	-10	-70	-	-
535	78	32	3	96	-	-
625	97	122	22	2684	-	-
400	60	-103	-15	-1545	-	-
425	70	-78	-5	-390	-	-
$\Sigma = 5,030$	750	0	0	6305	41410	1,318

$\bar{X} = 503$
$\bar{Y} = 75$

$$r_{xy} = \frac{\Sigma xy}{\sqrt{\Sigma x^2 y^2}}$$

$$= \frac{6305}{7387.7181}$$

$$= .85$$

2. The researcher in question 1 is also interested in finding out if there is a relationship between English aptitude scores (X) and Algebra grades earned (Y). Using the raw score formula (5.3) calculate the correlation coefficient.

X	Y	XY	X^2	Y^2
580	65	37,700	336,400	4,225
520	85	44,200	270,400	7,225
470	70	32,900	-	-
465	80	37,200	-	-
500	65	32,500	-	-
510	80	40,800	-	-
535	70	37,450	-	-
625	78	48,750	-	-
400	65	26,000	-	-
425	92	39,100	-	-
$\Sigma = 5030$	750	376,600		57048

2571500

$$r_{xy} = \frac{N\Sigma XY - \Sigma X\Sigma Y}{\sqrt{[N\Sigma X^2 - (\Sigma X)^2][N\Sigma Y^2 - (\Sigma Y)^2]}}$$

$$= \frac{(10)(376,600) - (5030)(750)}{\sqrt{[(10)(2571500) - (5030)^2][(10)(57,048) \cdot (750)^2]}}$$

$$= \frac{3,766,000 - 3,772,500}{\sqrt{[25715000 - 25,300,900][570480 - 562500]}}$$

$$= \frac{-6500}{\sqrt{(414,100)(7980)}} \qquad = \frac{-6500}{57,485}$$

$$= -0.11$$

3. In exercise 1 we found the correlation between English aptitude scores and grades earned to be 0.85. What proportion of the total variance in grades can be associated with the variance in aptitude scores?

$$r^2 = (0.85)^2$$
$$= .7225$$

Chapter 5 Exercises: Answers

1.

X	Y	x	y	xy	x^2	y^2
580	85	77	10	770	5,929	100
520	85	17	10	170	289	100
470	70	−33	−5	165	1,089	25
465	60	−38	−15	570	1,444	225
500	80	−3	5	−15	9	25
510	65	7	−10	−70	49	100
535	78	32	3	96	1,024	9
625	97	122	22	2,684	14,884	484
400	60	−103	−15	1,545	10,609	225
425	70	−78	−5	390	6,084	25
Σ = 5,030	750	0	0	6,305	41,410	1,318

$$r_{xy} = \frac{6,305}{\sqrt{(41,410)(1,318)}}$$

$$= \frac{6,305}{7,387.72}$$

$$= 0.85$$

2.

X	Y	XY	X^2	Y^2
580	65	37,700	336,400	4,225
520	85	44,200	270,400	7,225
470	70	32,900	220,900	4,900
465	80	37,200	216,225	6,400
500	65	32,500	250,000	4,225
510	80	40,800	260,100	6,400
535	70	37,450	286,225	4,900
625	78	48,750	390,625	6,084
400	65	26,000	160,000	4,225
425	92	39,100	180,625	8,464
$\Sigma = 5,030$	750	376,600	2,571,500	57,048

$$r_{xy} = \frac{10(376,600) - (5,030)(750)}{\sqrt{[10(2,571,500) - (5,030)^2][10(57,048) - (750)^2]}}$$

$$= \frac{3,766,000 - 3,772,500}{\sqrt{(414,100)(7,980)}}$$

$$= \frac{-6,500}{57,485}$$

$$= -0.11$$

3. $r^2 = (0.85)^2$
$= 0.7225$

Chapter 5 Mastery Test

1. a. The following scores were obtained from six individuals on variables X and Y. The variables are assumed to be interval in nature. Draw a scattergram of the data.

Variable X	x	Variable Y	y	xy
20	-15	11	4	-60
10	-25	12	5	-125
40	5	5	-2	-10
50	15	4	-3	-45
30	-5	7	0	0
60	25	3	-4	-100

$\mu_x = 35$

$\mu_y = 7$

$\Sigma x^2 = 1750$

$\Sigma y^2 = 70$

b. Explain the relationship between variables X and Y in terms of the shape of the scattergram.

c. Calculate the Pearson r.

2. a. Calculate the Pearson r for the following data.

$\mu_x = 4$

$\mu_y = 3.71$

Variable X/x		Variable Y/y		xy
1	-3	5	1.29	-5.87
2	-2	4	0.29	-0.58
3	-1	3	-0.71	0.71
4	0	2	-1.71	0
5	1	3	-0.71	-0.71
6	2	4	0.29	0.58
7	3	5	1.29	3.87

b. Draw a scattergram of the data and discuss the results in relation to the appropriate use of the Pearson r.

3. A researcher draws a large sample of students and computes the correlation coefficient between aptitude test scores and grade point average. The r is found to be $+0.63$. Suppose the researcher then correlates only the grade point averages of students with averages between 2.1 and 2.2 with their aptitude test scores. Would you expect the correlation to be approximately $+0.63$?

4. The scale of measurement of the correlation coefficient is the _____ scale. (interval, ordinal, or nominal)

5. Use the rules of thumb from the text to provide interpretation of the following values of r.
   a. $r = 0.89$
   b. $r = -0.34$
   c. $r = 0.56$
   d. $r = -0.21$

6. In problem 3, a researcher found a 0.63 correlation between aptitude test scores and grade point average. What proportion of the variance in grade point average is attributable to variables *other* than aptitude?

5.16

7. A researcher has found that high scores on a measure of anxiety are associated with high consumption of cigarettes for cigarette smokers. What is wrong with saying that high anxiety levels cause high consumption of cigarettes?

Chapter 5 Mastery Test: Answers

1. b. There appears to be a high negative linear relationship between variables X and Y. As scores on the X variable increase, scores on the Y variable tend to decrease.

   c. $r = -0.97$

2. a. $r = 0$

   b. The Pearson r is an inappropriate correlation coefficient due to the curvilinear relationship of these data.

3. The correlation coefficient would tend to be smaller because of the increased homogeneity of the group selected. The reduced number of individuals in the selected group would not affect the correlation coefficient.

4. ordinal

5. a. high positive correlation
   b. low negative correlation
   c. moderate positive correlation
   d. little, if any, correlation

6. $r^2 = (0.63)^2 = 0.40$ (the variance associated with differences in aptitude) $1 - 0.40 = 0.60$ (the variance associated with other factors)

7. Cause and effect cannot necessarily be inferred from even very high values of r.

6   Types of Correlation Coefficients

Comprehension Check

The following summary reviews the material presented in this chapter. To check your understanding of key concepts, supply the missing words indicated by the numbered blanks.

One of the most important considerations in selecting an appropriate correlation coefficient is the __(1)__ or __(2)__ of measurement of the variables to be correlated. Four types of measurement scales are considered in this chapter. A __(3)__ dichotomy is a variable scale that indicates the __(4)__ or __(5)__ of a particular characteristic. A __(6)__ dichotomy is a variable scale that describes an individual or score in a two-category classification where the variable is assumed to have underlying __(7)__. The ordinal scale is a scale of __(8)__ values. The __(9)__ and __(10)__ scales are combined in this discussion since they both exhibit the __(11)__ degree of __(12)__ in measurement. For both scales, the __(13)__ between levels of the __(14)__ on any part of the scale reflect __(15)__ in the characteristic being measured. Thus both scales have what are called __(16)__. The __(17)__ scale, however, has one additional property, that of a __(18)__ point.

The type of correlation coefficient used to determine the relationship between two __(19)__ is dependent upon the __(20)__ scale of __(21)__ of the variables. The appropriate correlation coefficient to use when both variables are measured on the interval or ratio scale is the __(22)__ coefficient. The point-biserial correlation coefficient should be used when one variable is measured on an __(23)__ or __(24)__ scale and the other variable is a __(25)__. The __(26)__ coefficient is calculated when both variables are discrete dichotomies. The __(27)__ is used when both variables are measured on ordinal scales, and is calculated by using the __(28)__ scores of the variables. The point-biserial, phi, and Spearman rho are correlation coefficients that are special cases of the __(29)__ correlation coefficient.

There are also indices of relationships other than the __(30)__ coefficients. These include __(31)__ that can be used instead of the ones discussed above as well as coefficients that are also __(32)__ given the __(33)__ of the two variables correlated. For example, when both variables are measured on the __(34)__ scale, __(35)__ can be used as an alternative to the Spearman rho. When both variables are measured on a discrete- __(36)__ scale but both are not dichotomous, a __(37)__ table greater than 2 × 2 is needed to display the data. For these data, an appropriate correlation coefficient is the __(38)__. The __(39)__ coefficient is the appropriate correlation when both variables are dichotomous, have underlying continuity, and are normally distributed. When one variable is measured on the nominal-continuous scale and the other variable is measured on at least an interval scale, the appropriate correlation coefficient is the __(40)__. The rank-biserial correlation coefficient is used when one variable is measured on an __(41)__ scale and the other variable is a __(42)__.

The use of all the above correlation coefficients assumes that the relationship between the two variables is __(43)__. This __(44)__ of linearity in the relationship __(45)__ always hold for variables in the behavioral sciences. When the assumption __(46)__ be met, the use of the above coefficients is not __(47)__. Should the Pearson product-moment coefficient be applied when there is a __(48)__ trend in the data, the coefficient will __(49)__ the relationship between the two variables.

An index of the __(50)__ between two variables that have a curvilinear relationship is the __(51)__ coefficient. Eta can have only positive values between __(52)__ and __(53)__. Like the Pearson product-moment coefficient, the __(54)__ of the eta coefficient equals the proportion of the __(55)__ in the one variable that can be __(56)__ to the variance in the second variable.

Comprehension Check: Answers

1. level
2. type
3. nominal-discrete
4. presence
5. absence
6. nominal-continuous
7. continuity
8. ranked
9. interval
10. ratio
11. same
12. precision
13. differences
14. categories
15. equal differences
16. equal units
17. ratio
18. known zero
19. variables
20. measurement
21. each
22. Pearson product-moment
23. interval
24. ratio
25. discrete dichotomy
26. phi
27. Spearman rho
28. ranked
29. Pearson product-moment
30. product-moment
31. coefficients
32. appropriate

33. measurement scales
35. Kendall's tau
37. contingency
39. tetrachoric
41. ordinal
43. linear
45. does not
47. appropriate
49. underestimate
51. eta
53. +1
55. variance

34. ordinal
36. nominal
38. contingency coefficient
40. biserial
42. discrete dichotomy
44. assumption
46. cannot
48. nonlinear
50. relationship
52. 0
54. square
56. attributed

Chapter 6 Exercises

1. a. A child psychologist examined the impact of sibling status upon the age at which infants begin to walk. The following data were obtained for 16 toddlers, with 1 or 0 indicating the presence or absence of an older child within the home. Compute the point-biserial correlation coefficient and explain the meaning of your answer.

Infant	Older Sibling(s)	Walking Age (months)
A	1	11.2
B	1	12.4
C	0	15.6
D	0	12.3
E	1	10.8
F	0	16.1
G	1	13.2
H	1	11.8
I	0	14.1
J	0	12.5
K	0	15.3
L	0	13.8
M	1	14.1
N	0	16.0
O	1	11.4
P	1	12.0

Note: The point-biserial coefficient is the appropriate correlation for this exercise because one variable is a discrete dichotomy and the other variable is measured on at least an interval scale.

$$r_{pb} = \frac{\mu_1 - \mu_0}{\sigma_y} \sqrt{pq}$$

$$\mu_1 = \frac{11.2 + \cdots + 12.0}{8}$$

$$= \frac{12.11 - }{} \sqrt{(0.5)(\quad)}$$

$$=$$

$$= (-1.37)(\quad)$$

$$\mu_0 = \frac{}{}$$

$$=$$

$$=$$

$$\sigma_y = \sqrt{\frac{\Sigma Y^2 - \dfrac{(\Sigma Y)^2}{N}}{N}}$$

$$= \sqrt{\frac{2871.5 - \dfrac{(\quad)^2}{}}{}}$$

$$= \sqrt{\frac{2871.5 - }{}}$$

$$= \sqrt{\frac{}{16}}$$

$$=$$

$$p = \quad ; q =$$

Hint: μ_1 is the mean walking age for children with older sibling(s).

μ_0 is the mean walking age for children without older sibling(s).

σ_y is the standard deviation of *all* walking scores (ages).

b. A teacher has developed a new test of achievement, and believes that one question is strongly related to the amount of knowledge students have about the subject. The teacher wants to see if there is a relationship between the total test score and a correct answer to that question (1) rather than the incorrect answer (0). Compute the point-biserial correlation coefficient.

Student	Test Score	Question
1	95	1
2	87	1
3	70	0
4	74	1
5	82	1
6	68	0
7	92	0
8	60	1
9	75	1
10	83	1

2. a. A political pollster wishes to provide some insight into an upcoming election. One hundred area residents are asked to indicate whether they voted for the incumbent candidate in the past election, and whether they favor the individual for re-election. Use the following information to compute the phi coefficient and explain the meaning of your answer.

Last election *voted for/will vote for* this election	46
Last election *voted for/will not vote for* this election	14
Last election *did not vote for/will vote for* this election	12
Last election *did not vote for/will not vote for* this election	28

This Election

		Will not vote for	Will vote for	
Last Election	Voted for	14	48	60
	Did not vote for	28	12	40
		42	58	100

$$\phi = \frac{BC - AD}{\sqrt{(A + B)(C + D)(A + C)(B + D)}}$$

$$= \frac{(46)(\ ) - (\ )(\ )}{\sqrt{(\ )(\ )(\ )(\ )}}$$

$$= \frac{-168}{\sqrt{\ }}$$

$$= \frac{\ }{\ }$$

$$=$$

Hint: In a 2 × 2 contingency table the cells are labeled this way:

A	B
C	D

b. A researcher in consumer products wants to see if there is a relationship between smoking and sex. A sample of 100 adults provided the following data. Compute the phi coefficient and explain the meaning of your answer.

Men, smokers	29
Men, nonsmokers	21
Women, smokers	18
Women, nonsmokers	32

3. a. The fifteen graduates of a dental hygiene program are ranked according to their scores on the clinical and written portions of their state board examination. Compute the Spearman rho correlation coefficient.

Graduate	Clinical Rank	Written Rank	d	d^2
A	4	5	−1	1
B	12	11	1	1
C	8	8	–	–
D	6	3	–	–
E	5	10	–	–
F	1	4	–	–
G	15	13	–	–
H	14	14	–	–
I	11	15	–	–
J	3	1	–	–
K	2	2	–	–
L	7	6	–	–
M	9	7	–	–
N	10	9	–	–
O	13	12	–	–
			$\Sigma d =$	$\Sigma d^2 =$

$$\rho = 1 - \frac{6\Sigma d^2}{N(N^2 - 1)}$$

$$= 1 - \frac{6(\ \ )}{15[(\ \ )^2 - \ ]}$$

$$= 1 - \frac{}{15(\ \ )}$$

$$= 1 -$$

$$=$$

Hints: The sum of the differences between the paired ranks is always zero. Use caution when squaring a negative number because the squared answer is positive. The N in the calculation formula is the number of *paired* observations.

b. In a pet show, the judging of a particular breed of dog is determined by color and body shape. Use the results of the judging to compute rho.

Dog	Color	Body Shape
1	4	3
2	8	7
3	1	4
4	5	8
5	2	1
6	6	5
7	3	2
8	7	6

4. a. A high school teacher examined the relationship between reading skill and typing speed. The following speeds were attained by 12 first-year students, with 1 indicating their ability and 0 their lack of ability to read at a given level of proficiency at the beginning of the course. Compute the biserial correlation coefficient.

Student	Reading Proficiency	Typing Speed (wpm)
A	1	45
B	0	32
C	0	35
D	0	26
E	1	38
F	1	41
G	0	37
H	1	44
I	0	25
J	1	31
K	1	41
L	0	34

$$r_b = \frac{\mu_1 - \mu_0}{\sigma_y} \frac{pq}{u}$$

$$= \left(\frac{\quad}{\quad}\right)\left[\frac{(\ )(\ )}{\quad}\right]$$

$$= \left(\frac{8.5}{\quad}\right)\left(\frac{\quad}{\quad}\right)$$

$$= (\quad)(\quad)$$

$$=$$

$$\mu_1 =$$

$$\mu_0 =$$

$$\sigma_y = \sqrt{\frac{\quad - \frac{(\quad)^2}{\quad}}{12}}$$

$$= \sqrt{\frac{\quad}{12}}$$

$$= \sqrt{\quad}$$

$$=$$

$$p = \quad ; q = \quad ; u =$$

Hint: The hints to exercise 1 apply to this exercise. The symbol u represents the height of the unit normal curve at the point of division between the p and q proportions under the curve.

b. A teacher is interested in the relationship between hours of television watched in the week prior to an examination and whether students passed or failed the examination. Compute the biserial correlation coefficient.

Student	TV Hours	Examination
A	6	1
B	14	0
C	9	1
D	20	0
E	22	0
F	17	1
G	13	1
H	4	1
I	11	1
J	19	0
K	8	0
L	16	1

5. a. A secondary school administrator examined the relationship between the success of graduating seniors in receiving advanced placement credit in mathematics and their success in receiving advanced placement credit in a natural science. The following data are available for 80 recent graduates who attempted to receive credit in each, with success or lack of success dependent upon their scores on a standardized examination. Assume a normal distribution of scores with underlying continuity, and compute the tetrachoric correlation coefficient. (Note: In this exercise we have two variables, both of which are dichotomies. Both mathematics and science variables have underlying continuity in knowledge of the subject matter. However, some point has been established to determine which scores warrant advanced placement and which do not.)

		Mathematics Advanced Placement	
		Success	Lack of Success
Science Advanced Placement	Lack of Success	23	30
	Success	18	9

$$\frac{BC}{AD} = \frac{(\ )(\ )}{(\ )(9)}$$

$$= \text{———}$$

$$=$$

$$r_{\text{tet}} =$$

Hint: In a contingency table such as the one above, the table could have been set up as follows:

	Success	Lack of Success
Success		
Lack of Success		

This would not have changed the magnitude of the relationship, but it would affect the sign of the value. Try it.

b. A grade school teacher made the following observations about the height and weight of students in the class. What is the relationship between height and weight? Explain your answer.

		Height	
		Tall	Short
Weight	Heavy	12	7
	Slender	8	8

6. a. A college mathematics instructor examined the impact of high school calculus exposure upon the level of achievement in the first-semester freshman course. Fifteen students are ranked according to their final scores, and categorized as to whether they have had (1) or have not had (0) previous exposure. Compute the rank-biserial correlation coefficient.

Student	Previous Exposure	Class Rank
A	1	1
B	1	2
C	0	3
D	1	4
E	0	5

F	0	.	6
G	0		7
H	1		8
I	0		9
J	1		10
K	1		11
L	0		12
M	0		13
N	0		14
O	1		15

$$r_{rb} = \frac{2}{N}(\mu_1 - \mu_0) \qquad \mu_1 =$$

$$\mu_0 =$$

$$= \frac{2}{\quad}(\quad - \quad)$$

$$= 0.133(\quad)$$

$$=$$

Hint: N in the computation formula is the number of bivariate or paired observations.

b. A graduate level course in a university has listed a recommended but not required lower level course. The instructor wants to determine if having taken the lower level course affects graduate class standing. Compute the appropriate correlation coefficient. Explain your answer.

Class Standing	Course Level
1	1
2	0
3	1
4	1
5	1
6	0
7	1
8	0
9	0

$$r_{rb} =$$

7. An industrial psychologist wants to investigate the relationship between the age of workers and their performance at a particular type of job. The workers' ages are categorized into intervals of equal width. The mean performance scores for each category are determined as is the mean performance score for the total group.

The sum of deviation scores squared for the categories is 48.32. The sum of deviation scores squared for the total group is 79.53. Compute the eta coefficient.

$$\eta = \sqrt{1 - \frac{\Sigma(Y - \mu_c)^2}{\Sigma(Y - \mu_t)^2}}$$

$$= \sqrt{1 - \underline{\quad\quad}}$$

$$=$$

Chapter 6 Exercises: Answers

1. a. $r_{pb} = \dfrac{12.11 - 14.46}{1.71} \sqrt{(0.5)(0.5)}$

$$= (-1.35)(0.5)$$

$$= -0.675$$

$$\mu_1 = \frac{11.2 + 12.4 + 10.8 + 13.2 + 11.8 + 14.1 + 11.4 + 12.0}{8}$$

$$= 12.11$$

$$\mu_0 = \frac{15.6 + 12.3 + 16.1 + 14.1 + 12.5 + 15.3 + 13.8 + 16.0}{8}$$

$$= 14.46$$

$$\sigma_y = \sqrt{\frac{2871.5 - \dfrac{(212.6)^2}{16}}{16}}$$

$$= \sqrt{\frac{2871.5 - 2824.9}{16}}$$

$$= \sqrt{\frac{46.6}{16}}$$

$$= 1.71$$
$$p = 0.50$$
$$q = 0.50$$

There is a moderate negative relationship between presence of an older child and walking age. The children assigned a zero (no older sibling) tend to have higher age scores, and children with older sibling(s) in the home tend to walk at a younger age.

b. $r_{pb} = \dfrac{79.43 - 76.67}{10.57} \sqrt{(0.7)(0.3)}$

$$= 0.12$$

2. a.

Last Election	This Election		
	Will not vote for	Will vote for	
Voted for	14	46	60
Did not vote for	28	12	40
	42	58	100

$$\phi = \frac{(46)(28) - (14)(12)}{\sqrt{(60)(40)(42)(58)}}$$

$$= \frac{1288 - 168}{\sqrt{5846400}}$$

$$= \frac{1120}{2417.9}$$

$$= 0.46$$

There is a low positive correlation between people who voted for the incumbent last election and people who plan to vote the same way this election.

b.

	Men	Women	
Smokers	29	18	47
Nonsmokers	21	32	53
	50	50	100

$$\phi = \frac{(18)(21) - (29)(32)}{\sqrt{(47)(53)(50)(50)}}$$

$$= \frac{-550}{2495.5}$$

$$= -0.22$$

There is little correlation between sex and smoking.

3. a. $\Sigma d = 0$ $\Sigma d^2 = 76$

$$\rho = 1 - \frac{6(76)}{15[(15)^2 - 1]}$$

$$= 1 - \frac{456}{15(224)}$$

$$= 1 - .136$$

$$= 0.86$$

b. $\rho = 1 - \dfrac{6(24)}{8(64 - 1)}$

$$= 0.71$$

4. a. $r_b = \left(\dfrac{40 - 31.5}{6.23}\right)\left[\dfrac{(0.5)(0.5)}{0.3989}\right]$

$$= \left(\frac{8.5}{6.23}\right)\left(\frac{0.25}{0.3989}\right)$$

$$= (1.36)(0.627)$$

$$= 0.85$$

$\mu_1 = 40$

$\mu_0 = 31.5$

$$\sigma_y = \sqrt{\dfrac{15{,}803 - \dfrac{(429)^2}{12}}{12}}$$

$$= \sqrt{\dfrac{15{,}803 - 15{,}336.75}{12}}$$

$$= \sqrt{38.85}$$

$$= 6.23$$

$p = 0.5$

$q = 0.5$

$u = 0.3989$

b. $r_b = \left(\dfrac{10.86 - 16.60}{5.52}\right)\left[\dfrac{(0.583)(0.487)}{0.3902}\right]$

$$= -0.65$$

5. a.

	Success	Lack of Success
Lack of Success	23	30
Success	18	9

$$\frac{BC}{AD} = \frac{(30)(18)}{(23)(9)}$$

$$= \frac{540}{207}$$

$$= 2.61$$

$$r_{\text{tet}} = 0.36$$

b. $r_{\text{tet}} = -0.21$

There is little or no relationship between height and weight.

6. a. $r_{rb} = \dfrac{2}{15}(7.29 - 8.63)$ $\mu_1 = 7.29$

$$= 0.133(-1.34)$$ $\mu_0 = 8.63$

$$= -0.18$$

b. $r_{rb} = -0.50$

The lower level class has a moderate correlation with class rank. Thus for this group, the students that took the lower level course tended to rank higher.

7. $\eta = \sqrt{1 - \dfrac{48.32}{79.53}}$

$$= 0.63$$

Chapter 6 Mastery Test

1. a. For the phi correlation coefficient, specify the conditions that must be satisfied for a value of $+1$ or -1 to be possible.

   b. Do these conditions also apply to the tetrachoric correlation coefficient?

2. Which correlation coefficient may sometimes assume values greater than $+1$, and values less than -1?

3. On a ten-point spelling test, one word was spelled correctly (1) or incorrectly (0). What is the value of the appropriate correlation coefficient for the relationship between spelling the one word and a student's test score?

Student	One word	Test score
A	1	3
B	1	5
C	1	8
D	1	6
E	0	2
F	0	4
G	0	3
H	0	6
I	0	5
J	0	7
K	0	3
L	0	4

4. Assume that the values 4 (correct spelling) and 3 (incorrect spelling) had been assigned to the dichotomous variable in problem 3. What effect would this have on the value of the correlation coefficient?

5. What effect would reversing the assignment of zero and one have on the value of the correlation coefficient?

6. In all cases, how does the value of the biserial correlation coefficient compare in magnitude to the value of the point-biserial correlation coefficient?

7. Why is the contingency coefficient (C) a more useful index of relationship than the phi coefficient (ϕ)?

8. If $p = 0.35$ and $r_{pb} = 0.62$, find r_b.

9. What impact may tied ranks have upon the value of the Spearman rho correlation coefficient?

10. What is the range of values for the eta coefficient, and how does η^2 compare with r^2?

11. What is the range of values for the rank-biserial correlation coefficient?

12. A special education teacher believes that there is a relationship between the popularity of students as rated by their peers and the comparative ranking of serious disruptions caused by the students. The following data were obtained, with 1 representing the most popular student, 2 the next most popular, and so on. Calculate the appropriate correlation coefficient.

Student	Peer-rated popularity	Number of disruptions
A	1	2
B	2	4
C	3	7
D	4	5
E	5	12
F	6	6
G	7	10
H	8	9

13. A psychologist is interested in the relationship between scholastic achievement and social achievement for ninth-grade students. A study of 100 students provided the following student characteristics. Compute the appropriate correlation coefficient.

high scholastic and high social achievement	35 students
high scholastic and low social achievement	20 students
low scholastic and high social achievement	20 students
low scholastic and low social achievement	25 students

Chapter 6 Mastery Test: Answers

1. a. $(A + B) = (C + D)$ and $(A + C) = (B + D)$

   b. No. The r_{tet} can have values of $+1$ and -1 when $(A + B) \neq (C + D)$ or $(A + C) \neq (B + D)$.

2. Biserial correlation coefficient.

3. $r_{pb} = 0.34$

4. No effect. $r_{pb} = 0.34$

5. The magnitude of r_{pb} is the same; however, it is a negative value. In this question $r_{pb} = -0.34$.

6. The biserial is always greater than the point-biserial.

7. Use of the phi coefficient (ϕ) is restricted to 2×2 contingency tables, while the contingency coefficient (C) can be used for contingency tables greater than 2×2, such as 3×4.

8. $r_b = 0.80$

9. The maximum value may be less than ± 1.

10. Eta may have values from 0 to $+1$. η^2 is always equal to or greater than r^2. Both η^2 and r^2 indicate the proportion of variance in one variable that can be attributed to the variance in the other variable.

11. The range of r_{rb} is from $+1$ to -1.

12. $\rho = 0.74$
    Note: The Spearman rho is used when both variables are measured on ordinal scales. The number of disruptions for students needs to be ranked with the least number of disruptions given a value of 1.

13.

	Social Achievement	
	low	high
Scholastic Achievement high	20	35
low	25	20

$r_{tet} = 0.30$

7 Introduction to Inferential Statistics: Part I

Comprehension Check

−7 (90%)

(1) parameter
(2) statistic
(3) information
(4) all members
(5) sample
(6) inferences
(7) parameter
(8) statistic
(9) inferential statistics
probability (random)
(10) random (probability)
(11) member
(12) chance
(13) independent
(14) probability
(15) kth
(16) convenient
(17) list
(18) sampling fraction
(19) sample
(20) population
(21) member
(22) members (one)
(23) sample
(24) multiples
(25) added
(26) random (individual)
(27) subgroups
(28)

The following summary reviews the material presented in this chapter. To check your understanding of key concepts, supply the missing words indicated by the numbered blanks.

In Chapter 1 we define a ___(1)___ as a descriptive measure of a population and a ___(2)___ as a descriptive measure of a sample. In behavioral science research, the ideal situation would be to base the ___(3)___ of an investigation upon ___(4)___ from the entire population. Since it is not always feasible to gather information on all members of the population, the alternative is to select a ___(5)___ and make ___(6)___ about the population ___(7)___ from knowledge of the sample ___(8)___. This chain of reasoning from statistics to parameters is part of what is called ___(9)___.

There are several important concepts related to the chain of reasoning of inferential statistics. The first of these relates to methods of sampling. The most commonly discussed method of sampling is called simple ___(10)___ sampling. It is defined as a ___(11)___ sample selected in such a manner that each ___(12)___ or element of the population has an equal ___(13)___ of selection and that all members of the sample are selected ___(14)___ of one another.

Systematic sampling is also a ___(15)___ sample in which every ___(16)___ member of the population is selected. Systematic sampling is more ___(17)___ than simple random sampling when a ___(18)___ of the population members is readily available. The procedure involves determining the ___(19)___, defined as $1/k$, or the ratio of the size of ___(20)___ to the size of the ___(21)___. This means that for every kth ___(22)___ of the population, ___(23)___ will be selected for the sample. The process begins by randomly selecting a number between 1 and k. This becomes the first member of the ___(24)___. Subsequent members of the sample are ___(25)___ of the sampling fraction that are ___(26)___ to this first random number.

Cluster sampling is used when the selection of ___(27)___ members of a large population is impractical. It involves the random selection of ___(28)___

(29) homogeneous
(30) strata
(31) sampling
(32) stratum
(33) stratified
(34) sample
(35) population
(36) conclusions
(37) higher
(38) reject
(39) probability
(40) hypothesis
(41) accept
(42) fluctuation
(43) reject
(44) different
(45) Tenability
(46) sampling distribution (underlying)
(47) central limit
(48) normal
(49) μ
(50) parameter
(51) $\frac{\sigma^2}{n}$
(52) $\frac{\sigma}{\sqrt{n}}$
(53) sample
(54) appropriate (inappropriate)
(55) t distribution
(56) $n-1$
(57) sample
(58) normal
(59) hypothesis (a priori)

or intact groups of individuals from a population of clusters. When a cluster is selected for the sample, each member of the cluster is included in the sample.

For each of the previously mentioned sampling procedures the population is assumed to be generally __(29)__ . However, if the researcher can assume that the population is heterogeneous with several homogeneous subpopulations, called __(30)__ , then it may be possible to carry out an appropriate __(31)__ procedure within each __(32)__ . Such a sampling procedure is referred to as __(33)__ sampling. It is important to note that one result of stratified sampling is representativeness of the sample. Members from each identified stratum will be included in the __(34)__ , thus providing for sampling throughout the entire __(35)__ .

An additional concept related to the chain of reasoning of inferential statistics is probability. The concept of probability is important since it provides the basis for __(36)__ when testing hypotheses about population parameters. For example, suppose that a college admissions director hypothesizes the average verbal SAT score of the freshmen to be 485. To test the hypothesis, the director randomly selects 150 entering freshmen and finds the average verbal SAT score to be 498. Even though the sample mean is __(37)__ than the hypothesized value for the population mean, is the difference sufficient for the admissions director to __(38)__ the hypothesis? To answer this question, it is necessary to find the __(39)__ of obtaining a sample mean of 498 by chance when in fact the __(40)__ is true. If the probability is quite high, the director would __(41)__ the hypothesis and would attribute the difference between the sample mean and the hypothesized value to sampling __(42)__ . If the probability is quite low, the director would __(43)__ the hypothesis and would conclude that the average verbal SAT score is __(44)__ from 485. It is important to note that in hypothesis testing, we do not prove or disprove the hypothesis. We retain or reject the __(45)__ of the hypothesis.

The basic concept involved in retaining or rejecting a hypothesis is the __(46)__ of all possible outcomes. We use the __(47)__ theorem to determine this distribution. The theorem states that the distribution of all possible sample means of a given sample size is __(48)__ ; has a mean equal to __(49)__ , the population __(50)__ ; and has variance equal to __(51)__ . The standard deviation of this distribution, __(52)__ , is called the standard error of the mean. However, when the population variance is unknown and is estimated by the variance of the __(53)__ , the normal curve is __(54)__ for describing this sampling distribution of the mean. The appropriate distribution is the __(55)__ for __(56)__ degrees of freedom, where n is the size of the __(57)__ . As the sample size increases to 120 or greater, the Student's t-distribution approximates the __(58)__ distribution.

The process of testing hypotheses is based upon the researcher's ability to establish logically an __(59)__ for the population. This value is usually established through ___(60)___ of the research literature and previous research ___(61)___ with the variables under investigation. The process of statistical estimation involves estimation of the population ___(62)___ based upon the knowledge of the sample ___(63)___. A sample statistic, such as the sample mean, is called a ___(64)___ estimate of the population parameter. More commonly in inferential statistics, we use the point estimate to determine a range of values called an ___(65)___, that we are confident contains the ___(66)___ being estimated. Such an interval is called a ___(67)___. For example, the 95 percent confidence interval, denoted ___(68)___, is the range of values that we are 95 percent confident contains the ___(69)___.

Comprehension Check: Answers

1. parameter
2. statistic
3. results
4. data
5. sample
6. inferences
7. parameters
8. statistics
9. inferential statistics
10. random
11. probability
12. member
13. probability
14. independently
15. probability
16. kth
17. convenient
18. listing
19. sampling fraction
20. sample
21. population
22. member
23. one
24. sample
25. multiples
26. added
27. individual
28. clusters
29. homogeneous
30. strata
31. sampling
32. stratum
33. stratified
34. sample
35. population
36. decision-making
37. greater
38. reject
39. probability
40. hypothesis
41. retain
42. fluctuation
43. reject
44. different
45. tenability
46. underlying distribution
47. central limit
48. normal
49. μ
50. parameter
51. σ^2/n
52. $\sigma/\sqrt{n}$
53. sample
54. inappropriate
55. Student's t-distribution
56. $n-1$
57. sample
58. normal
59. a priori value
60. knowledge
61. experience
62. parameter

63. statistic
64. point
65. interval
66. parameter
67. confidence interval
68. CI_{95}
69. population parameter

Chapter 7 Exercises

1. a. A college dormitory population is made up of the following numbers of students. Describe a method of obtaining a 5 percent *random* sample of this population. The sample is to be gathered without replacement.

	Male	Female
Freshmen	1700	1300
Sophomore	1500	1000
Junior	1400	1100
Senior	1200	800

   b. Describe a method of obtaining a 5 percent *systematic* sample.

   c. Describe a method of obtaining a 5 percent *stratified* sample.

2. In a large college freshman chemistry class, 196 students took the final examination. The scores were found to be approximately normally distributed; the mean score was 70 and the standard deviation was 8.

   a. What is the probability of a student's receiving a score between 62 and 78?

   b. What is the probability of a student's receiving a score of 54 or less?

   c. What is the probability of a student's receiving a score of 84 or greater?
   Hint: You may want to draw the sampling distribution of the mean in order to determine this probability.

3. a. If we treated all chemistry classes in the college as a population, repeatedly drew samples of 196 students, and developed a frequency distribution of all possible sample means, this would be a distribution of sample means or the theoretical sampling

distribution of means. The standard deviation of the theoretical sampling distribution is called the ⎯⎯⎯⎯ ⎯⎯⎯⎯ of the ⎯⎯⎯⎯.

b. Describe the following for the distribution of sample means.
   (1) Shape
   (2) Location
   (3) Variability

4. In exercise 2, a sample of 196 students had a mean examination score of 70 and the standard deviation was 8. The point estimate for the population of all chemistry classes is ⎯⎯⎯⎯. Develop the 95 percent confidence interval for the population of chemistry classes.

$$CI = \bar{X} \pm (t)(s_{\bar{X}})$$ $\bar{X} =$

$$CI_{95} = \pm (\quad)(\quad)$$ $t =$

$$= \pm$$

$$= (\quad , \quad)$$ $s_{\bar{X}} = \dfrac{s}{\sqrt{}} = \dfrac{}{\rule{1cm}{0.4pt}} =$

5. The principal of a high school believes that students are brighter than average. A nationally normed achievement test has a mean of 100. A random sample of 50 students takes the test. A test scoring service reports the mean score to be 110 and the sum of the squares of the deviation scores to be 2,050.

a. What is the hypothesis?
b. What is the alternative hypothesis?
c. What is the estimated standard error of the mean?

$$s_{\bar{X}} = \dfrac{s}{\sqrt{}} \qquad s = \sqrt{\dfrac{\rule{1.5cm}{0.4pt}}{n-1}}$$

$$= \dfrac{}{7.07} \qquad = \sqrt{\dfrac{}{49}}$$

$$= \qquad\qquad =$$

6. The director of the mathematics curriculum of a school district believes that students will have an average score of 75 on a particular examination. For a random sample of 26 students the mean score is 72, and the standard deviation of these scores is 10. The level of significance is established at .10.

a. What is the hypothesis?
b. What is the alternate hypothesis?
c. What is the estimated standard error of the mean?

$$s_{\bar{x}} = \frac{s}{\sqrt{n}}$$

$$= \underline{\quad\quad}$$

$$=$$

d. On a diagram of the curve of the sampling distribution identify (1) the location of the hypothesized population mean, (2) the location of the sample mean, and (3) the area under the curve below the sample value.

$$t = \frac{\bar{X} - \mu}{s_{\bar{X}}}$$

$$= \frac{72 - 75}{1.96}$$

$$= -1.53$$

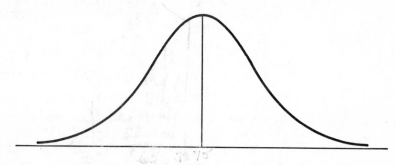

e. Develop the 90 percent confidence interval.

$$CI_{90} = \quad \pm (\quad)(\quad)$$
$$= \quad \pm$$
$$= (68.65, \quad)$$

Hint: Note the number of students in the sample, the directionality of the alternate hypothesis, and the level of significance.

7. a. Suppose the curriculum director in exercise 6 had tripled the sample size to 78 students, and this larger sample has the same mean and standard deviation. The estimated standard error of the mean is:

$$s_{\bar{x}} = \frac{s}{\sqrt{n}}$$

$$= \underline{\quad\quad}$$

$$=$$

b. On a diagram of the curve for the sampling distribution identify (1) the location of the hypothesized population mean, (2) the location of the sample mean, and (3) the area under the curve below the sample value.

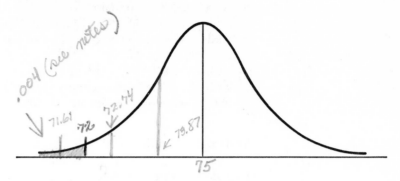

c. Develop the 90 percent confidence interval.

$CI_{90} = 72 \pm ($ $)($ $)$

$\phantom{CI_{90}} = 72 \pm$

$\phantom{CI_{90}} =$

Chapter 7 Exercises: Answers

1. a. The dormitory population totals 10,000 students and a 5 percent sample would be 500 students. Each student could be identified by a number and with the use of a table of random numbers, a sample of 500 students selected.

   b. The college has or develops an alphabetical list of all dormitory students. The sample size is 500 and the sampling fraction is 500/10,000 or 1/20. The researcher selects a random number between 1 and 20, for example 12. The twelfth student on the list is the first member of the sample, and the other members of the sample are identified by adding multiples of 20 to 12. The second member of the sample is number 32, the third is number 52, and so on until 500 students are selected.

   c. The strata or subpopulations are male and female students in each college class, or a total of 8 strata. We would need to take proportional allocations from each stratum, and in this case a 5 percent random or systematic sample from each stratum. The sample would be made up of 85 male and 65 female freshmen, 75 male and 50 female sophomores, 70 male and 55 female juniors, and 60 male and 40 female seniors.

2. a. The scores 62 to 78 are one standard deviation below and above the mean. The probability would be .3413 + .3413, or .6826.

   b. The score of 54 is two standard deviations below the mean and this area under the normal curve is .4772. The remaining area under the curve is .5000 − .4772, or .0228, which is the probability of receiving a score of 54 or less.

   c. The score of 84 is 1.75 standard deviations above the mean and this area under the normal curve is .4599. The probability of receiving a score of 84 or greater is .5000 − .4599, or .0401.

3. a. standard error of the mean

   b. (1) A normal distribution.
      (2) The mean of this distribution of sample means equals the population mean.
      (3) The variance of the distribution of sample means equals the population variance divided by the sample size (σ^2/n). The standard deviation of the distribution (standard error of the mean) is given by $\sigma/\sqrt{n}$ and estimated by $s/\sqrt{n}$.

4. The point estimate is 70.
$$CI = \bar{X} \pm (t)(s_{\bar{X}})$$
$$CI_{95} = 70 \pm (1.96)(0.57)$$
$$= 70 \pm 1.12$$
$$= (68.88, 71.12)$$
$$\bar{X} = 70$$
$$t = 1.96$$

$$s_{\bar{X}} = \frac{s}{\sqrt{n}} = \frac{8}{\sqrt{196}} = 0.57$$

5. a. $H_0: \mu = 100$
   b. $H_a: \mu > 100$

   c. $s_{\bar{X}} = \dfrac{s}{\sqrt{n}}$

   $$= \frac{6.47}{7.07}$$

   $$= 0.92$$

   $$s = \sqrt{\frac{\Sigma(X - \bar{X})^2}{n - 1}}$$

$$= \sqrt{\frac{2050}{49}}$$

$$= 6.47$$

6. a. $H_0: \mu = 75$

b. $H_a: \mu \neq 75$

c. $s_{\bar{X}} = \frac{10}{\sqrt{26}} = 1.96$

d.

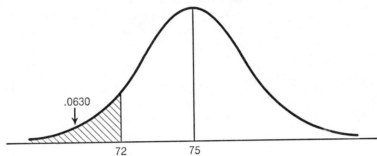

.0630

72   75

e. $CI_{90} = 72 \pm (1.708)(1.96)$

$= 72 \pm 3.35$

$= (68.65, 75.35)$

7. a. $s_{\bar{X}} = \frac{10}{\sqrt{78}}$

$= 1.13$

b.

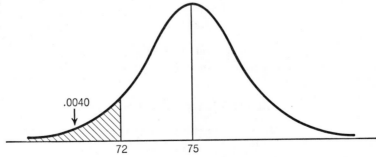

.0040

72   75

c. $CI_{90} = 72 \pm (1.667)(1.13)$
$= 72 \pm 1.88$
$= (70.12, 73.88)$

Chapter 7 Mastery Test

1. Suppose you are the director of research for a state educational system that is made up of diverse population characteristics. You have been directed to assess the English achievement for all eighth grade students in the state. The achievement test you are to use costs $4.25 per unit. Since you have $6,800 budgeted for purchase of the test, you will be able to test 1,600 students. What would be the most practical sampling procedure to use in this investigation if the average class size is 32 students?

2. Based upon a review of the literature, a researcher believes that the mean English achievement score for eighth grade students is 73. Write this hypothesis in null form.

3. Suppose you believe the mean student English achievement score to be 73 and you draw a random sample of 125 students. The sample mean is found to be 71; the standard deviation of these scores is 20. You establish the level of significance at .05. Would you retain or reject your hypothesis? Why?

4. Develop CI_{99} for the data presented in problem 3.

5. Suppose the sample size in problem 3 to be 31 rather than 125. Develop CI_{90} for the data. With this confidence interval and a level of significance of .10, would you retain or reject the null hypothesis?

6. For the data in problem 3, what is the probability of finding a sample mean of less than 71?

Chapter 7 Mastery Test: Answers

1. Stratified cluster sampling would probably be the best method. The budgeted amount of $6,800 will purchase 1,600 tests which is enough to sample 50 classrooms. Classrooms will be used as clusters to expedite testing and to reduce confusion that could result from

random individual student sampling. The classrooms to be sampled would be proportionally stratified around the state to provide the most representative sample.

2. $H_0: \mu = 73$ or $H_0: \mu - 73 = 0$

3. $\mu = 73$

   $\bar{X} = 71$

   $s_{\bar{x}} = \dfrac{20}{\sqrt{125}}$

   $= 1.79$

   $t = \dfrac{2}{1.79}$

   $= 1.12$

   Retain the null hypothesis.
   The probability of observing a sample mean of 71, when in fact the population mean is 73, is greater than the level of significance. The difference between the sample mean and the population mean may be attributed to sampling fluctuation.

4. $(66.38, 75.62)$

5. $(65.09, 76.91)$
   Retain H_0.

6. .1314

8 Introduction to Inferential Statistics: Part II

Comprehension Check

The following summary reviews the material presented in this chapter. To check your understanding of key concepts, supply the missing words indicated by the numbered blanks.

The term hypothesis may be defined as a ___(1)___ about one or more population parameters. The usual strategy is to test the ___(2)___ hypothesis against an ___(3)___ hypothesis. The alternative hypothesis, the ___(4)___ outcome of the research investigation, can only be shown by ___(5)___ the null hypothesis. In this process of testing the null hypothesis, we do not ___(6)___ or disprove a hypothesis. Rather, the accepted research convention is to determine the ___(7)___ of a hypothesis.

As noted in Chapter 7, a hypothesis can be developed for a single ___(8)___ (the one-sample case) or for two parameters (the ___(9)___-sample case). For both the one-sample and two-sample cases, establishment of the ___(10)___ hypothesis is the crucial step in the process of testing the ___(11)___ hypothesis. Alternative hypotheses can be either ___(12)___ or ___(13)___. In the two-sample case, a nondirectional alternative hypothesis states that there is a ___(14)___ in the hypothesized population values, but the ___(15)___ is not specified. A directional alternative hypothesis states that there is a ___(16)___ in hypothesized values and specifies the ___(17)___ of this difference. Testing the ___(18)___ hypothesis against a ___(19)___ alternative is a more ___(20)___ test.

In inferential statistics we make decisions about parameters based upon knowledge of the corresponding ___(21)___ value. We are ___(22)___ certain about the value of a parameter because the entire ___(23)___ has not been measured. In hypothesis testing, the decision is made to ___(24)___ or not ___(25)___ the hypothesis. Depending upon the decision, there is a possibility of making one of two types of errors. If a true hypothesis is rejected, a ___(26)___ error is made. If a false hypothesis is retained (not rejected), a ___(27)___ error is made. Both types of errors are serious and should be minimized in any research.

The probability of making a Type I error when the null hypothesis is rejected is, by definition, the __(28)__. Holding other factors constant, increasing the probability of a Type I error __(29)__ the probability of making a Type II error. Lowering the level of significance __(30)__ the probability of making a Type II error. The usual research convention is to establish the __(31)__ when the hypotheses are formulated. The most frequently used levels of significance are __(32)__ and __(33)__. If the null hypothesis is rejected at one of these levels, the researcher must realize that a Type I error may be made __(34)__ percent or __(35)__ percent of the time. Other α-levels are appropriate, depending upon the __(36)__ of making either a Type I or Type II error.

The "region of rejection" in hypothesis testing is determined by the __(37)__ of the alternate hypothesis. For a nondirectional alternative, the region of rejection is in __(38)__ of the distribution. For a directional alternate hypothesis, the region of rejection is in __(39)__ of the distribution. The critical values of the __(40)__ are those values that represent the beginning of the region of rejection in the underlying distribution. When the observed value of the test statistic exceeds the critical value, the null hypothesis is __(41)__.

In developing confidence intervals, the __(42)__ is defined as the confidence the researcher has that the interval contains the __(43)__ being estimated. The level of confidence used in most research settings is the complement of the __(44)__ that would have been used in the comparable test of the hypothesis. For example, if α were set at .10 for the test of a hypothesis, the level of confidence used in the estimate of the parameter would be .90.

Comprehension Check: Answers

1. conjecture
2. null
3. alternative
4. desired
5. rejecting
6. prove
7. tenability
8. parameter
9. two
10. alternative
11. null
12. nondirectional
13. directional
14. difference
15. direction
16. difference
17. direction
18. null
19. directional
20. powerful
21. sample
22. never
23. population
24. reject
25. not to reject (to retain)
26. Type I
27. Type II
28. level of significance
29. decreases
30. increases
31. level of significance
32. .05

33. .01
34. five
35. one
36. consequences
37. directionality
38. two tails
39. one tail
40. test statistic
41. rejected
42. level of confidence
43. parameter
44. level of significance

Chapter 8 Exercises

1. A college sociologist reviewed a study of student beer consumption and found the average consumption to be 48 ounces per week. The sociologist believes that students who are members of certain social organizations imbibe more than their peers. What are the hypothesis and alternate hypothesis for this study?

   H_0: μ

   H_a: μ

2. Another individual on the same campus (exercise 1) does not believe that there is a difference in consumption between members of certain social organizations and the student body at large. What are the null and alternate hypotheses?

   H_0:

   H_a:

3. A genetic botanist is striving to produce a specific type of miniature apple tree with fruit of normal size. The average mature height of the original apple tree is 20 feet. What are the hypothesis and alternate hypothesis for this study?

   H_0:

   H_a:

4. The director of instructional development in a school district has read about declining scores for twelfth grade students on a certain nationally normed test. This school district has adopted new teaching methods to improve student achievement and the director wants to know if the methods affect student scores. If the mean of the national test is 78, what are the hypothesis and alternate hypothesis for this study?

   H_0:

   H_a:

5. A graduate student hypothesizes that the mean income for a population is $6,800. The population mean income, in fact, is $6,800. The graduate student rejects the hypothesis. Has an error been made, and if so, what type of error?

6. The graduate student in exercise 5 hypothesizes the mean age for the population to be 47. In fact, the population mean is not 47. The graduate student rejects the hypothesis. Has an error been made, and if so, what type of error?

7. The graduate student further hypothesizes that the average family size in the population is 4.3 members. The population mean family size, in fact, is grossly different from 4.3 but the hypothesis is retained. Has an error been made, and if so, what type of error?

8. Suppose the same graduate student is willing to take 5 chances out of 100 of being incorrect in the hypothesis decision making process. The student has established the level of significance at

   _____.

9. a. A student believes a population to have a mean age of 47. A random sample of 150 people drawn from the population has a mean age of 49.4 and has a sample standard deviation of 13. Draw the sampling distribution of the means for this hypothesis, and identify the position of the sample mean.

$$44.88$$

$$-1s_{\bar{X}}$$

$$s_{\bar{X}} =$$

$$=$$

Hint: The center point in the distribution is the population parameter.

b. What is the probability of finding a sample of size 150 with a mean age of 49.4 when the true population mean age is 47:

$$t = \frac{\overline{X} - \mu}{s_{\overline{X}}}$$

$$= \underline{\hspace{2cm}}$$

$$= \underline{\hspace{1cm}}$$

The probability is _____.

10. The shaded areas in the following graph illustrate the region of rejection in terms of standard errors using the normal curve for a two-tailed test at the .05 level of significance.

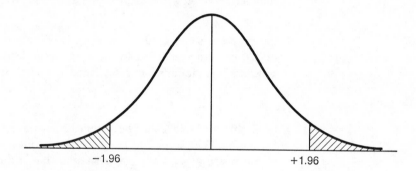

Provide an illustration similar to the one above for each of the following stated hypotheses and compute the critical value(s) for each.

a. H_0: $\mu = 47$
   H_a: $\mu \neq 47$
   .10 level of significance

b. H_0: $\mu = 6800$
   H_a: $\mu > 6800$
   .01 level of significance

c. H_0: $\mu = 6800$
   H_a: $\mu \neq 6800$
   .02 level of significance

d. H_0: $\mu = 4.3$
   H_a: $\mu < 4.3$
   .05 level of significance

Hint: In any hypothesis testing situation, it is the alternate hypothesis that determines the location of the region of rejection. The level of significance establishes the size of the region of rejection. It is expressed in terms of standard errors and provides us with generalized critical values (cv).

11. Suppose the test statistic (t) were $+2.11$ for each of the parts in exercise 10. Would you reject or retain the null hypotheses?
Hint: If the test statistic exceeds the critical value, reject the hypothesis.

12. Suppose the test statistic (t) is -2.11. Would you reject or retain the null hypotheses in exercise 10?

13. For each of the following levels of significance, indicate the level of confidence and the critical value. Use the normal curve as the underlying distribution.

Level of Significance	Level of Confidence	Critical Value
.05	.95	1.96
.10	–	–
.01	–	–
.20	–	–

Hint: In developing confidence intervals, the level of confidence is the complement of the level of significance.

14. Using the t-distributions as the underlying distribution, indicate for each of the following the level of confidence and the critical value.

Level of Significance	Degrees of Freedom	Level of Confidence	Critical Value
.05	20	–	2.086
.05	200	.95	–
.10	27	–	–
.01	10	–	–

15. a. Assume that $\bar{X} = 30.2$, $s = 5.3$ and $n = 25$. Test the null hypothesis, at the .05 level of significance, against the alternate hypothesis that μ is less than 32.
$H_0: \mu =$
$H_a: \mu <$

$$s_{\bar{X}} = \frac{s}{\sqrt{n}}$$

$$= \frac{}{\sqrt{}}$$

$$=$$

$$t = \frac{\bar{X} - \mu}{s_{\bar{X}}}$$

$$= \frac{30.2 - }{}$$

$$=$$

$$t_{cv} =$$

Hint: The critical value of the test statistic is influenced by the level of significance, the directionality of the alternate hypothesis and the degrees of freedom.

b. Do you retain or reject the hypothesis?
Hint: If the test statistic exceeds the critical value of the test statistic, the hypothesis is rejected. If t does not exceed t_{cv}, the hypothesis is retained.

c. Construct the 95 percent confidence interval for the actual value of the population mean.

$$CI_{95} = \quad \pm (\quad)(\quad)$$
$$= \quad \pm 2.19$$
$$= (28.01, \quad)$$

Hint: The statistic is the sample mean. The standard error of the statistic is the standard error of the mean or $s_{\bar{X}}$. The confidence interval is developed symmetrically around the statistic. Thus, the critical value from the tables uses the value of the level of significance for both tails of the distribution for the appropriate degrees of freedom.

Chapter 8 Exercises: Answers

1. $H_0: \mu = 48$
   $H_a: \mu > 48$

2. $H_0: \mu = 48$
   $H_a: \mu \neq 48$

3. H_0: $\mu = 20$
   H_a: $\mu < 20$

4. H_0: $\mu = 78$
   H_a: $\mu \neq 78$
   In this exercise, the director would probably not be justified in using a directional alternate hypothesis.

5. Yes, a Type I error.

6. No, the decision is proper.

7. Yes, a Type II error.

8. 5 percent.

9. a.

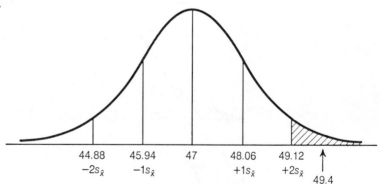

$$s_{\bar{x}} = \frac{13}{\sqrt{150}}$$
$$= 1.06$$

b. $t = \dfrac{49.4 - 47}{1.06} = 2.26$

$p = .0119$

10. a.

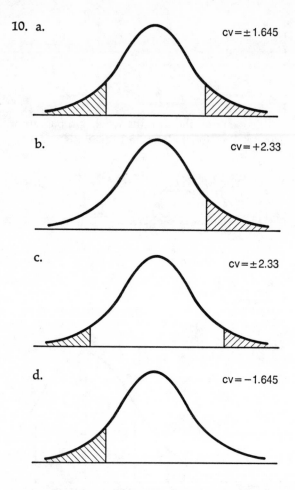

cv = ± 1.645

b.

cv = + 2.33

c.

cv = ± 2.33

d.

cv = − 1.645

11. a. reject b. retain c. retain d. retain

12. a. reject b. retain c. retain d. reject

13. .05   .95   1.96
    .10   .90   1.645
    .01   .99   2.58
    .20   .80   1.28

14. .05   20   .95   2.086
    .05   200   .95   1.96
    .10   27   .90   1.703
    .01   10   .99   3.169

15. a. H_0: $\mu = 32$
   H_a: $\mu < 32$

   $$s_{\bar{X}} = \frac{5.3}{\sqrt{25}}$$

   $$= 1.06$$

   $$t = \frac{30.2 - 32}{1.06}$$

   $$= -1.70$$

   $$t_{cv} = -1.71$$

   b. retain

   c. $CI_{95} = 30.2 \pm (2.064)(1.06)$
   $$= 30.2 \pm 2.19$$
   $$= (28.01, 32.39)$$

Chapter 8 Mastery Test

1. Determine the null and alternative hypotheses for each of the following statements.

   a. The average sixth-grader watches television more than twelve hours per week.

   b. A college placement officer believes engineering graduates receive higher starting salaries than accounting graduates.

   c. Sermons at Protestant services and Roman Catholic services are of equal length.

   d. A researcher believes that young girls and boys have different growth patterns, and that boys on average are shorter than girls at a certain age. A random sample of 25 boys has a mean height of 32.3 inches, while a random sample of 25 girls has a mean height of 33.1 inches.

2. A college freshman mathematics teacher is concerned about the background knowledge of entering students and is overheard to say, "Every year the SAT scores go down and down. Last year the mean was 476, and this year I'll bet it's lower." A random sample of freshman has a mean mathematics SAT score of 469

   a. The hypothesis is tested by appropriate methods and found to be barely tenable. The teacher feels safe in saying, "Indeed, the scores are declining." Has the teacher made an error? If so, what type of error?

   b. Another teacher examines the data and finds a small mathematical error that makes the hypothesis untenable. However, this teacher questions the methodology used in the sample, and so retains the null hypothesis. Has this teacher made an error? If so, what type of error?

3. A student in nutrition has been reading that people, on the average, are taller due to better diets. Some literature states that the mean height of adult men and women is 67 inches, but the student believes that these data underestimate the true situation. A sample of 30 adults has a mean height of 69 inches and a standard deviation of 6.0 inches. The student is willing to take only a 5 percent chance of making a Type I error.

   a. What are the values for the test statistic and the critical value of the test statistic?

   b. Should the student retain or reject the hypothesis?

4. a. If a null hypothesis is rejected at the .05 level of significance, what, if anything, can be said about its rejection or retention at the .01 level of significance?

   b. If a null hypothesis is retained at the .05 level of significance, what, if anything, can be said about its rejection or retention at the .01 level of significance?

   c. If a null hypothesis is rejected at the .01 level of significance, what, if anything, can be said about its rejection or retention at the .05 level of significance?

   d. If a null hypothesis is retained at the .01 level of significance, what, if anything, can be said about its rejection or retention at the .05 level of significance?

5. Assume that the 95 percent confidence interval for a population mean is (28.2, 36.6). What is the 99 percent confidence interval?

Chapter 8 Mastery Test: Answers

1. a. $H_0: \mu = 12$ b. $H_0: \mu_E = \mu_A$

   $H_a: \mu > 12$ $H_a: \mu_E > \mu_A$

   c. $H_0: \mu_P = \mu_{RC}$ d. $H_0: \mu_{boys} = \mu_{girls}$

   $H_a: \mu_P \neq \mu_{RC}$ $H_a: \mu_{boys} < \mu_{girls}$

2. a. Yes, a Type I error. (If the null hypothesis is tenable, the alternate hypothesis cannot be supported.)

   b. Yes, a Type II error. (If the null hypothesis is not tenable, it should be rejected in favor of the alternate hypothesis.)

3. a. $\mu = 67$, $\bar{X} = 69$, $s_{\bar{X}} = 1.10$, $t = +1.82$, $t_{cv} = \pm 1.699$

   b. reject

4. a. May or may not reject at $\alpha = .01$, depending upon the value of the test statistic.

   b. retain

   c. reject

   d. May or may not retain at $\alpha = .05$, depending upon the value of the test statistic.

5. $CI_{99} = (26.88, 37.92)$

9   Hypothesis Testing: One-Sample Case

Comprehension Check

The following summary reviews the material presented in this chapter. To check your understanding of key concepts, supply the missing words indicated by the numbered blanks.

This chapter deals with testing hypotheses and constructing confidence intervals for a single mean, correlation, proportion, or variance. The following questions provide a logical structure for testing hypotheses and for constructing the corresponding confidence intervals.

1. What __(1)__ is being tested?
2. What are the hypothesized __(2)__ and the corresponding sample __(3)__ ?
3. What are the sampling __(4)__ of the statistic and the __(5)__ of the statistic?
4. What is the __(6)__ of the test statistic for the specified level of significance?
5. What is the __(7)__ of the confidence interval for the specified level of confidence?
6. What is the conclusion?

The general formula (9.2) for testing hypotheses is:

$$\text{Test Statistic} = \frac{\underline{(8)} - \underline{(9)}}{\underline{(10)}}$$

The general formula (9.4) for the corresponding confidence interval is:

$$\text{CI} = \underline{(11)} \pm (\underline{(12)})(\underline{(13)})$$

When testing the null hypothesis H_0: $\mu = a$ and when the population variance __(14)__ is unknown and is __(15)__ by s^2, the appropriate underlying distribution is the Student's __(16)__ for __(17)__ degrees of freedom. In the process of testing this hypothesis, the observed value of the test statistic, __(18)__ , is compared to the __(19)__ . The critical value of t is dependent upon three factors: the level of __(20)__ , the __(21)__ of the hypothesis and the ___(22)___ (n − 1). If the observed value of t exceeds the ___(23)___ (t_{cv}), the null hypothesis is ___(24)___ .

The shape of the sampling distribution of the correlation coefficient varies with the value of ρ. As ρ departs substantially from ___(25)___ , the ___(26)___ distribution becomes exceedingly ___(27)___ . However, if we ___(28)___ the correlation coefficients using Fisher's log transformation, the sampling distribution of the transformed correlation coefficients approximates the ___(29)___ distribution regardless of the value of ___(30)___ and the size of the ___(31)___ . The ___(32)___ of the transformed correlation coefficient is given by $1/\sqrt{n-3}$.

To construct confidence intervals for the correlation coefficient, the normal distribution should be used as the ___(33)___ distribution. The interval is first constructed for the ___(34)___ values of $r(z_r)$, and then the endpoints of the interval are converted back to ___(35)___ values.

The sampling distribution for a proportion is the ___(36)___ distribution. However, the ___(37)___ distribution can be used as an approximation of the binomial distribution for ___(38)___ samples. The criterion used to determine whether the sample is sufficiently ___(39)___ to use the ___(40)___ distribution is the product ___(41)___ or $(n)(q)$, whichever is the ___(42)___ . This product must be larger than five.

To test the null hypothesis H_0: $\sigma^2 = a$, the appropriate underlying distribution is the ___(43)___ for $n-1$ ___(44)___ . Unlike the normal distribution and the Student's t-distributions, the χ^2 distribution is ___(45)___ symmetrical. Thus, when testing the null hypothesis against a ___(46)___ alternative, there are ___(47)___ distinct critical values of the test statistic.

Related to the chain of reasoning for inferential statistics is the concept of statistical precision. Technically, statistical precision is the ___(48)___ of the standard error of the sampling distribution. In other words, as the standard error ___(49)___ , the statistical precision ___(50)___ . Statistical precision can be increased by ___(51)___ the ___(52)___ of the sample. With a large sample, we have a more ___(53)___ estimate of the population parameter since it is based upon a greater number of observations. In addition, when testing hypotheses, adequate statistical precision is likely to result in the ___(54)___ of the ___(55)___ hypothesis when in fact it is false. Thus statistical precision is of paramount importance to inferential statistics.

Comprehension Check: Answers

1. hypothesis
2. parameter
3. statistic
4. distribution
5. standard error
6. critical value
7. critical value
8. Statistic
9. Parameter
10. Standard Error of the Statistic
11. Statistic
12. Critical Value
13. Standard Error of the Statistic
14. σ^2

15. estimated
16. t-distribution
17. $n - 1$
18. t
19. critical value
20. significance
21. nature
22. degrees of freedom
23. critical value
24. rejected
25. zero
26. sampling
27. skewed
28. transform
29. normal
30. ρ
31. sample
32. standard error
33. underlying
34. transformed
35. r
36. binomial
37. normal
38. large
39. large
40. normal
41. $(n)(p)$
42. smaller
43. χ^2 distribution
44. degrees of freedom
45. not
46. nondirectional
47. two
48. inverse
49. decreases
50. increases
51. increasing
52. size
53. precise
54. rejection
55. null

Chapter 9 Exercises

1. A director of graduate studies believes that the mean age of graduate students today has changed from what it was five years ago when it was 29. A sample of 43 graduate students selected randomly has a mean age of 32.6 and a standard deviation of 7.3. The level of significance is set at .05.

   a. What hypothesis is being tested?
      H_0: $\mu =$
      H_a: $\mu \neq$

   b. What are the hypothesized parameter and the corresponding sample statistic?
      $\mu =$
      $\overline{X} =$

   c. What are the sampling distribution of the statistic and the standard error of the statistic?

$$s_{\bar{x}} = \frac{s}{\sqrt{n}} \qquad t = \frac{\bar{X} - \mu}{s_{\bar{x}}}$$

$$= \underline{\hspace{1cm}} \qquad = \frac{\underline{\hspace{2cm}}}{\underline{\hspace{1cm}}}$$

$$= \underline{\hspace{1cm}} \qquad = \underline{\hspace{1cm}}$$

d. What is the critical value of the test statistic?

$t_{cv} =$

Hint: Consider the sample size, the directionality of the alternate hypothesis, and the level of significance. You might want to draw a sketch of the sampling distribution to locate the region of rejection.

e. What is the critical value for the confidence interval?

cv =

CI = Statistic $\pm$ (critical value)(standard error of the statistic)

$CI_{95} = \qquad \pm (\quad)(\quad)$

$\phantom{CI_{95}} = \qquad \pm$

$\phantom{CI_{95}} = (\qquad\qquad)$

f. What is the conclusion? Give a brief explanation.

2. A distraught professor asserts that students at the university devote less than 10 hours per week to out-of-class study. A questionnaire is distributed to a sample of 300 students. The results show an average allotment of 14.8 hours per week and the standard deviation of the sample is 4.6 hours. Test the authenticity of the professor's assertion at the .10 level of significance. Construct the 90 percent confidence interval for the population parameter.

a. What hypothesis is being tested?

$H_0: \mu$

$H_a: \mu <$

b. What are the hypothesized parameter and the corresponding sample statistic?

$\mu =$

$\bar{X} =$

c. What are the sampling distribution of the statistic and the standard error of the statistic?

$$s_{\bar{X}} = \frac{s}{\sqrt{n}} \qquad t = \frac{\bar{X} - \mu}{s_{\bar{X}}}$$

$$= \frac{\quad}{\quad} \qquad\qquad = \frac{\quad}{\quad}$$

$$= \qquad\qquad\qquad =$$

d. What is the critical value of the test statistic?
$t_{cv} =$
Hint: The H_a: is directional.

e. What is the critical value for the confidence interval?
cv =
$CI_{90} = \qquad \pm (\quad)(\quad)$
$\qquad\quad = \qquad \pm$
$\qquad\quad = (\quad , \quad)$
Hint: The CI is symmetric.

f. What is the conclusion? Give a brief explanation.

3. The personnel director of a large corporation believes there is a high (0.75) correlation between selected employee salary levels and their number of years of professional education. In a random sample of 61 employees the correlation was found to be 0.64. The director establishes the level of significance at .05 in order to test the hypothesis.

a. What hypothesis is being tested?
$H_0: \rho =$
$H_a: \rho$

b. What are the hypothesized parameter and the corresponding sample statistic?
$\rho =$
$r =$
Hint: Remember to transform the correlation coefficients.

c. What are the sampling distribution and the standard error of the statistic?

$$s_{z_r} = \sqrt{\frac{1}{n - 3}} \qquad z = \frac{z_r - z_\rho}{s_{z_r}}$$

$$= \sqrt{\frac{\quad}{\quad}} \qquad\qquad = \frac{\quad}{\quad}$$

$$= \qquad\qquad\qquad\qquad =$$

d. What is the critical value of the test statistic?

e. What is the critical value for the confidence interval?

cv =

$$CI_{95} = \quad \pm (\quad)(\quad)$$
$$= \quad \pm$$
$$= (\quad , \quad)$$
$$= (\quad , \quad)$$

Hint: The interval is calculated by using transformed values that need to be changed back to r values.

f. What is the conclusion? Briefly explain.

4. A foreign language teacher believes that the time required to attain a given level of comprehension is inversely proportional to the age at which the learning process begins. Fifty French students of varying ages participated in a study. A correlation coefficient of −0.45 was found. Test (at the .10 level of significance) the teacher's research hypothesis that the correlation between age and learning time is smaller than −0.40. Construct a 90 percent confidence interval for the population parameter.

a. What hypothesis is being tested?
H_0:
H_a:

b. What are the hypothesized parameter and the corresponding sample statistic?

$$= \qquad z_\rho =$$
$$r = \qquad =$$

Hint: Be careful to carry the negative sign throughout the calculations.

c. What are the sampling distribution of the statistic and the standard error of the statistic?

$$s_{z_r} = \sqrt{\frac{1}{n-3}} \qquad z = \frac{z_r - z_\rho}{s_{z_r}}$$

$$= \sqrt{\frac{1}{}} \qquad = \frac{ - }{}$$

$$= \qquad =$$

d. What is the critical value of the test statistic?

$z_{cv} =$

Hint: Check the directionality of the H_a:

e. What is the critical value for the confidence interval?

cv =

CI = $\pm ($)( )

= $\pm$

= (,) z_r form

= (,) r form

Hint: With a directional H_a: the cv and t_{cv} are not the same value.

f. What is the conclusion? Briefly explain.

5. The director of student housing at a college wants to know if there is a relationship between the scores of freshmen students on a "quality-of-dorm-life" scale and their parents' level of income. The dormitory life scale is constructed so that high scores indicate a more positive attitude toward dormitory living. A sample of 47 freshmen is selected randomly and the sample correlation coefficient is found to be .289. Test the null hypothesis H_0: $\rho = 0$, against the nondirectional alternative H_a: $\rho \neq 0$, at the .10 level of significance. What is your conclusion?

6. Suppose the state director of education believes that less than 25 percent of school principals are women. To test this conjecture, a random sample of 75 principals reveals that 15 are women. The level of significance is set at .05.

a. What hypothesis is being tested?

H_0: $P =$

H_a: P

b. What are the hypothesized parameter and the corresponding sample statistic?

$P =$

$p = \underline{\quad} =$

Hint: Be careful with the use of capital P and lower case p.

c. What are the sampling distribution of the statistic and the standard error of the statistic?

$$s_p = \sqrt{\frac{pq}{n}} \qquad\qquad z = \frac{p - P}{s_p}$$

$$= \sqrt{\frac{(\quad)(\quad)}{}} \qquad\qquad = \frac{-}{}$$

$$= \qquad\qquad\qquad =$$

d. What is the critical value of the test statistic?

$z_{cv} =$

e. What is the critical value for the confidence interval?

cv =

$CI_{95} = \qquad \pm (\quad)(\quad)$

$= \qquad \pm$

$= (\quad , \quad)$

f. What is the conclusion? Explain briefly.

7. Campaign managers believe that their candidates' views on a controversial issue are supported by more than 75 percent of the area voters. A survey is conducted using a 500 member sample and a total of 393 voters express approval. Test the given hypothesis at the .10 level of significance using the appropriate directional alternative hypothesis. Construct a 90 percent confidence interval for the population parameter.

a. What hypothesis is being tested?

H_0:

H_a:

b. What are the hypothesized parameter and the corresponding sample statistic?

$P =$

$p =$

c. What are the sampling distribution of the statistic and the standard error of the statistic?

$s_p = \sqrt{\dfrac{(\quad)(\quad)}{\quad}} \qquad z = \dfrac{-}{\quad}$

$= \qquad\qquad =$

d. What is the critical value of the test statistic?

e. What is the critical value for the confidence interval?

cv =

$CI = \qquad \pm (\quad)(\quad)$

$= \qquad \pm$

$= (\quad , \quad)$

f. What is your conclusion? Explain briefly.

8. A researcher at a university has observed that the mean SAT score for applicants has changed over the past five years. The researcher wonders if the variability of scores has also changed. Five years ago, the applicant SAT scores had a standard deviation of 112. A sample of 30 applicants has a standard deviation of 98. The researcher sets the level of significance at .10.

   a. What hypothesis is being tested?
   H_0:
   H_a:
   Hint: Note how the variability in this problem is given and the form needed for hypothesis testing.

   b. What are the hypothesized parameter and the corresponding sample statistic?
   $\sigma^2 =$
   $s^2 =$

   c. What is the sampling distribution?

   d. What are the critical values of the test statistic?
   $\chi_{cv}{}^2 =$

   $$\chi^2 = \frac{(n-1)s^2}{a} \qquad s^2 = \text{sample variance}$$

   $$= \frac{(\quad)(\quad)}{} \qquad a = \text{hypothesized population variance}$$

   $$=$$

   Hint: Review the textbook for locating the critical values.

   e. What are the critical values for the confidence interval?
   $$\frac{(n-1)s^2}{\chi^2_{(1-\alpha/2)}} < \sigma^2 < \frac{(n-1)s^2}{\chi^2_{\alpha/2}}$$

   f. What is the conclusion? Explain briefly.

9. An English department chairperson, while emphasizing the need for a consistency of grading standards, selects ten faculty members to assign numerical grades following their review of a student essay. A variance of 85 is found. Does this support or refute, at the .10 level of significance, the chairperson's estimate of a population variance of 110? Construct a 90 percent confidence interval for the population variance.

a. What hypothesis is being tested?

H_0:

H_a:

b. What are the hypothesized parameter and the corresponding sample statistic?

c. What is the sampling distribution?

d. What are the critical values of the test statistic?

$$X_{cv}^2 =$$

$$\chi^2 = \frac{(\qquad)(\quad)}{}$$

$$=$$

e. What are the critical values for the confidence interval?

f. What is the conclusion?

Chapter 9 Exercises: Answers

1. a. H_0: $\mu = 29$

   H_a: $\mu \neq 29$

   b. $\mu = 29$

   $\overline{X} = 32.6$

   c. t-distribution with 42 degrees of freedom

   $$s_{\overline{x}} = \frac{7.3}{\sqrt{43}} \qquad t = \frac{32.6 - 29}{1.11}$$

   $$= 1.11 \qquad = 3.24$$

   d. $t_{cv} = \pm 2.019$

   e. cv $= 2.019$

   $CI_{95} = 32.6 \pm (2.019)(1.11)$

   $= 32.6 \pm 2.24$

   $= (30.36, 34.84)$

   f. Reject the null hypothesis; $p < .05$. The difference between the observed sample mean ($\overline{X} = 32.6$) and what the director hypothesized μ to be ($\mu = 29$) is too great to attribute to sampling error. Thus the null hypothesis is rejected at the .05 level of significance. The director can conclude with 95 percent confidence that the interval (30.36, 34.84) contains μ.

2. a. H_0: $\mu = 10$
   H_a: $\mu < 10$

   b. $\mu = 10$
   $\bar{X} = 14.8$

   c. t-distribution with 299 degrees of freedom

   $$s_{\bar{X}} = \frac{4.6}{\sqrt{300}} \qquad t = \frac{14.8 - 10}{0.27}$$
   $$= 0.27 \qquad = 17.78$$

   d. $t_{cv} = -1.282$

   e. cv $= 1.645$

   $$CI_{90} = 14.8 \pm (1.645)(0.27)$$
   $$= 14.8 \pm .44$$
   $$= (14.36, 15.24)$$

   f. Retain the null hypothesis; $p > .10$. The difference between the observed sample mean ($\bar{X} = 14.8$) and what the professor hypothesized μ to be ($\mu = 10$) is not sufficient to discount sampling error. Thus the null hypothesis is retained at the .10 level of significance. The professor can conclude with 90 percent confidence that the interval (14.36, 15.24) contains μ.
   Note: This exercise points out the problem that can result from careless development of the alternate hypothesis. Although the value of the test statistic is quite large, it is in the region of retention. The confidence interval helps the researcher to locate the true population mean.

3. a. H_0: $\rho = 0.75$
   H_a: $\rho \neq 0.75$

   b. $\rho = 0.75$ ($z_\rho = 0.973$)
   $r = 0.64$ ($z_r = 0.758$)

   c. The distribution is approximately normal.

   $$s_{z_r} = \sqrt{\frac{1}{61 - 3}} \qquad z = \frac{0.758 - 0.973}{0.131}$$
   $$= 0.131 \qquad = -1.64$$

d. Critical values are ± 1.96.

e. $cv = 1.96$

$$CI_{95} = 0.758 \pm (1.96)(0.131)$$
$$= 0.758 \pm 0.257$$
$$= (0.501, 1.015) \; z_r \text{ form}$$
$$= (0.463, 0.768) \; r \text{ form}$$

f. Retain the null hypothesis; $p > .05$. The difference between the sample correlation coefficient ($r = 0.64$) and what the personnel director hypothesized ρ to be ($\rho = 0.75$) is not sufficient to discount sampling error. Thus the null hypothesis is retained at the .05 level of significance. The personnel director can conclude with 95 percent confidence that the interval (0.463, 0.768) contains ρ.

4. a. $H_0: \rho = -0.40$
   $H_a: \rho < -0.40$

   b. $\rho = -0.40 \qquad z_\rho = -0.424$
      $r = -0.45 \qquad z_r = -0.485$

   c. The distribution is approximately normal.

   $$s_{z_r} = \sqrt{\frac{1}{50 - 3}} \qquad z = \frac{-0.485 - (-0.424)}{0.146}$$
   $$= 0.146 \qquad\qquad = \frac{-0.061}{0.146}$$
   $$= -0.418$$

   d. $z_{cv} = -1.28$

   e. $cv = 1.645$

   $$CI_{90} = -0.485 \pm (1.645)(0.146)$$
   $$= -0.485 \pm 0.240$$
   $$= (-0.245, -0.725) \; z_r \text{ form}$$
   $$= (-0.240, -0.620) \; r \text{ form}$$

   f. Retain the null hypothesis; $p > .10$. The difference between the sample correlation coefficient ($r = -0.45$) and what the teacher hypothesized ρ to be ($\rho = -0.40$) is attributed to sampling error. Thus the null hypothesis is retained at the .10 level of significance. The teacher can conclude with 90 percent confidence that the interval (-0.240, -0.620) contains ρ.

5. $t = r\sqrt{\dfrac{n-2}{1-r^2}}$

$= 0.28\sqrt{\dfrac{47-2}{1-0.084}}$

$= 2.026$

$t_{cv} = \pm 1.68$

Reject the null hypothesis; $p < .10$. The difference between the sample correlation coefficient ($r = 0.289$) and what the director hypothesized ρ to be ($\rho = 0$) is too great to attribute to sampling error. Thus the null hypothesis is rejected at the .10 level of significance. Referring to Appendix B.7 for 45 degrees of freedom the sample correlation of 0.289 exceeds the tabled value of 0.243 for a .10 level of significance.

6. a. H_0: $P = 0.25$

   H_a: $P < 0.25$

b. $P = 0.25$

   $p = \dfrac{15}{75} = 0.20$

c. The distribution is approximately normal.

   $s_p = \sqrt{\dfrac{(0.20)(0.80)}{75}} \qquad z = \dfrac{0.20 - 0.25}{0.0462}$

   $= 0.0462 \qquad\qquad\qquad = -1.08$

d. $z_{cv} = -1.645$

e. cv $= 1.96$

   $CI_{95} = 0.20 \pm (1.96)(0.0462)$

   $\qquad = 0.20 \pm 0.091$

   $\qquad = (0.109, 0.291)$

f. Retain the null hypothesis; $p > .05$. The difference between the sample proportion ($p = 0.20$) and what the state director of education hypothesized P to be ($P = 0.25$) is not sufficient to discount sampling error. Thus the null hypothesis is retained at the .05 level of significance. The director can conclude with 95 percent confidence that the interval (0.109, 0.291) contains P.

7. a. H_0: $P = 0.75$

   H_a: $P > 0.75$

b. $P = 0.75$
$p = 0.786$

c. The distribution is approximately normal.

$$s_p = \sqrt{\frac{(0.786)(0.214)}{500}} \qquad z = \frac{0.786 - 0.750}{0.018}$$

$$= 0.018 \qquad\qquad\qquad = 2.00$$

d. $z_{cv} = +1.282$

e. $cv = 1.645$
$$CI_{90} = 0.786 \pm (1.645)(0.018)$$
$$= 0.786 \pm 0.030$$
$$= (0.756, 0.816)$$

f. Reject the null hypothesis; $p < .10$. The difference between the sample proportion ($p = 0.786$) and what the campaign managers hypothesized P to be ($P = 0.75$) is too great to attribute to sampling error. Thus the null hypothesis is rejected at the .10 level of significance. The campaign managers can conclude with 90 percent confidence that the interval (0.756, 0.816) contains P.

8. a. $H_0: \sigma^2 = 12,544$
$H_a: \sigma^2 \neq 12,544$

b. $\sigma^2 = 12,544$
$s^2 = 9,604$

c. χ^2 distribution with 29 degrees of freedom

d. $\chi_{cv}^2 = 17.71$ and 42.56

$$\chi^2 = \frac{(n-1)s^2}{a}$$

$$= \frac{(30-1)(9,604)}{12,544}$$

$$= 22.20$$

e. $$\frac{(30-1)(9,604)}{42.56} < \sigma^2 < \frac{(30-1)(9,604)}{17.71}$$

$$CI_{90} = (6,544.08, \ 15,726.48)$$

f. Retain the null hypothesis; $p > .10$. The difference between the sample variance ($s^2 = 9{,}604$) and what the researcher hypothesized the variance to be ($\sigma^2 = 12{,}544$) is not sufficient to discount sampling error. Thus the null hypothesis is retained at the .10 level of significance. The researcher can conclude with 90 percent confidence that the interval (6,544.08, 15,726.48) contains σ^2.

9. a. $H_0: \sigma^2 = 110$
$H_a: \sigma^2 \neq 110$

b. $\sigma^2 = 110$
$s^2 = 85$

c. χ^2 distribution with 9 degrees of freedom.

d. $\chi_{cv}^2 = 3.32$ and 16.92

$$\chi^2 = \frac{(10 - 1)(85)}{110}$$

$$= 6.95$$

e. $\dfrac{(10 - 1)(85)}{16.92} < \sigma^2 < \dfrac{(10 - 1)(85)}{3.32}$

$CI_{90} = (45.11, 230.42)$

f. Retain the null hypothesis; $p > .10$. The difference between the sample variance ($s^2 = 85$) and what the chairperson hypothesized the variance to be ($\sigma^2 = 110$) is not sufficient to discount sampling error. Thus the null hypothesis is retained at the .10 level of significance. The chairperson can conclude with 90 percent confidence that the interval (45.11, 230.42) contains σ^2.

Chapter 9 Mastery Test

1. A nationally normed 25-item English test for third grade students has a reported mean score of 19.6. The director of English curriculum development for a school district believes students would score below average on this test. A sample of 30 students is selected randomly from the defined population and the test results are given to the director in raw data form as follows: $n = 30$, $\Sigma X = 525$, $\Sigma X^2 = 9{,}275$. Set the level of significance at .01.

   a. What hypothesis is being tested?

   b. What are the values of the test statistic and the critical value of the test statistic?

   c. Construct CI_{99}.

   d. What is the conclusion?

2. A grade school science teacher is concerned about the parental support for a new course, human development and growth, that is scheduled for next year. A random sample of 80 parents is selected and they are asked whether or not they support the teaching of this new course. Of those selected, 44 parents indicated they favored the new course. What is the teacher's estimate of the population proportion that supports the teaching of the course with the level of significance set at .20?

3. A physical education instructor at a military academy believes that 64 percent of the variance in weight of students can be associated with their variance in height. The instructor randomly selects 50 students and finds the height to weight relationship to be 0.74. The level of significance is set at .02.

   a. What hypothesis is being tested?

   b. What are the hypothesized parameter and the corresponding sample statistic?

   c. What are the sampling distribution and the standard error of the statistic?

   d. What is the critical value of the test statistic?

   e. What is the critical value for the confidence interval?

   f. What is the conclusion?

Chapter 9 Mastery Test: Answers

1. a. H_0: $\mu = 19.6$
   H_a: $\mu < 19.6$

b. $t = -6.56$
$t_{cv} = -2.462$

c. $CI_{99} = (16.62, 18.38)$

d. Reject H_0; $p < .01$. The curriculum director can be 99 percent confident that the interval (16.62, 18.38) contains the population mean.

2. $CI_{80} = (0.4787, 0.6213)$

3. a. H_0: $\rho = 0.80$
H_a: $\rho \neq 0.80$

b. $\rho = 0.80$ ($z_\rho = 1.099$)
$r = 0.74$ ($z_r = 0.950$)

c. The distribution is approximately normal.
$s_{z_r} = 0.146$
$z = -1.02$

d. ± 2.326

e. $cv = 2.326$.
$CI_{98} = (0.545, 0.860)$

f. Retain H_0; $p > .02$. The instructor can be 98 percent confident that the interval (0.545–0.860) contains the population corelation coefficient.

10 Hypothesis Testing: Two-Sample Case

Comprehension Check

The following summary reviews the material presented in this chapter. To check your understanding of key concepts, supply the missing words indicated by the numbered blanks.

In Chapter 9, the logic of testing hypothesis and estimating parameters was limited to the one-sample case. In Chapter 10 this logic is extended to the two-sample case. As before, it is based upon the concepts of sampling and probability theory as they relate to (1) the errors inherent in ___(1)___ testing, (2) the level of ___(2)___, and (3) the directional nature of the ___(3)___ hypothesis. The null hypothesis for the two-sample case is that there is no difference between two ___(4)___. For example, if we were testing the null hypothesis of no difference between population means, the ___(5)___ hypothesis would be H_0: ___(6)___. The alternative hypothesis may be either ___(7)___ $(H_a: \mu_1 \neq \mu_2)$ or ___(8)___ $(H_a: \mu_1 > \mu_2$ or $H_a: \mu_1 < \mu_2)$.

To test the null hypothesis for the two-sample case, the assumption of ___(9)___ samples is necessary. Under this assumption, the subjects in each of the two ___(10)___ are first drawn ___(11)___ from the ___(12)___ and then randomly assigned to the two ___(13)___ conditions. For example, the subjects could be randomly assigned to either the ___(14)___ group or the ___(15)___ group. Random assignment to the two conditions assures that the two groups are ___(16)___ before the experiment begins and that the ___(17)___ will not be confounded by ___(18)___ differences between the two groups.

For testing H_0: $\mu_1 = \mu_2$, the hypothesized ___(19)___ parameter is $\mu_1 - \mu_2$, or zero, and the corresponding sample ___(20)___ is $\bar{X}_1 - \bar{X}_2$, that is, the difference between the two sample ___(21)___. The ___(22)___ sampling distribution of the difference between sample means is defined by the central limit theorem. When the population variance (σ^2) is known, the ___(23)___ distribution is used as the underlying distribution. The standard deviation of the sampling distribution of sample means is called the ___(24)___ of the ___(25)___ and is based upon the assumption of ___(26)___ of ___(27)___; that is, the two populations have the same ___(28)___ (σ^2). However, when σ^2 is unknown and we can assume that the assumption of homogeneity of variance is true, we estimate the standard error of the difference by using the ___(29)___ estimate of the ___(30)___ (s^2). The underlying distribution is then the Student's ___(31)___ for ___(32)___ degrees of freedom. If the homogeneity of variance assumption cannot be made, an alternative procedure is used to estimate the ___(33)___ of the difference and an adjustment is made in the ___(34)___ of ___(35)___ associated with the ___(36)___ test.

In the above discussion of testing H_0: $\mu_1 = \mu_2$ it is assumed that we have ___(37)___ samples. An alternative procedure would be to have the subjects act as their own ___(38)___ or to have repeated measures taken on the same ___(39)___ under more than one treatment condition. Thus, for testing H_0: $\mu_1 = \mu_2$, we have ___(40)___ samples. The procedures for testing the null hypothesis for dependent samples are analogous to those for independent samples and are based upon the ___(41)___ theorem. The underlying distribution is ___(42)___ when σ^2 is known but is the ___(43)___ distribution with ___(44)___ degrees of freedom when σ^2 is unknown.

To test the null hypothesis of no difference between two ___(45)___ (H_0: $P_1 = P_2$) for independent and dependent samples the same procedures outlined for the two-sample case for the means are followed. The hypothesized population parameter is ___(46)___ and the corresponding sample statistic is the difference between the two sample proportions, ___(47)___ . The underlying distribution for testing H_0: $P_1 = P_2$ is the ___(48)___ distribution for both independent and dependent samples.

For testing H_0: $\rho_1 = \rho_2$, Fisher's log ___(49)___ must be used so that the ___(50)___ distribution can be used as the underlying distribution. The sample statistic is thus the difference between the ___(51)___ sample ___(52)___ coefficients, $z_{r_1} - z_{r_2}$. To develop the confidence interval, the interval is developed first around the difference between the ___(53)___ coefficients and then ___(54)___ back to values that reflect the difference between the observed sample correlation coefficients. For dependent samples, the correlation coefficients are ___(55)___ transformed and the ___(56)___ sample correlation coefficients are used. The underlying distribution of the test statistic for this test is the ___(57)___ with ___(58)___ degrees of freedom.

To test the null hypothesis H_0: $\sigma_1^2 = \sigma_2^2$ for two independent samples, the appropriate distribution is the ___(59)___ . The test statistic is the ___(60)___ of the two sample ___(61)___ . The specific F-distribution is determined by ___(62)___ values for ___(63)___ , $n_1 - 1$ and $n_2 - 1$ degrees of freedom. When we test against a nondirectional alternative, and the F-ratio is ___(64)___ than 1.0, the critical value of the ___(65)___ is the value in Appendix B.4. for ___(66)___ . When the F-ratio is less that 1.0, the critical value is the ___(67)___ of the tabled value for $\alpha/2$ and ___(68)___ respectively. The underlying distribution of the test statistic for testing the null hypothesis of the difference between population variances using dependent samples is the ___(69)___ with ___(70)___ degrees of freedom.

Comprehension Check: Answers

1. hypothesis
2. significance
3. alternative
4. population parameters
5. null
6. $\mu_1 = \mu_2$
7. nondirectional
8. directional
9. independent
10. samples
11. randomly
12. population
13. treatment
14. experimental
15. control
16. equivalent
17. treatment
18. initial
19. population
20. statistic
21. means
22. theoretical
23. normal
24. standard error
25. difference
26. homogeneity
27. variance
28. variance
29. pooled
30. population
31. t-distribution
32. $n_1 + n_2 - 2$
33. standard error
34. degrees
35. freedom
36. statistical
37. independent
38. controls
39. subjects
40. dependent
41. central limit
42. normal
43. t
44. $n - 1$
45. population proportions
46. $P_1 - P_2 = 0$
47. $p_1 - p_2$
48. normal
49. transformation
50. normal
51. transformed
52. correlation
53. transformed
54. converted
55. not
56. actual
57. t-distribution
58. $n - 3$
59. F-distribution
60. ratio
61. variations
62. two
63. degrees of freedom
64. greater
65. test statistics
66. $\alpha/2$
67. reciprocal
68. df_2 and df_1
69. t-distribution
70. $n - 2$

Chapter 10 Exercises

1. A psychologist wishes to determine whether the persistence of a child at a learning task is significantly affected by the presence of a parent within the learning environment. Two random samples of 15 members each are selected for participation in a study. The

average duration of effort among the children with at least one parent present is 27.3 minutes. Among the other children, the average duration of effort is 21.9 minutes. The standard deviations are 6.4 and 6.8 minutes, respectively. Test the hypothesis of no difference at the .01 level of significance. Use the nondirectional alternative hypothesis. Also construct the 99 percent confidence interval for the magnitude of the difference.

a. What hypothesis is being tested?

$H_0: \mu_1 =$

$H_a: \quad \neq$

b. What are the hypothesized parameter and the corresponding statistic?

$\mu_1 - \mu_2 =$

$\bar{X}_1 - \bar{X}_2 =$

c. What is the estimated standard error of the statistic?

$$s_{\bar{X}_1 - \bar{X}_2} = \sqrt{\frac{s^2}{n_1} + \frac{s^2}{n_2}} \qquad s^2 = \frac{(n_1 - 1)s_1^2 + (n_2 - 1)s_2^2}{n_1 + n_2 - 2}$$

$$= \sqrt{\frac{}{} + \frac{}{}} \qquad = \frac{(\quad - 1)(\quad)^2 + (\quad - 1)(\quad)^2}{\quad + \quad}$$

$$= \sqrt{\quad} \qquad = \frac{+ \ 647.36}{28}$$

$$= \qquad \qquad =$$

Hint: s^2 is the pooled estimate of the population variance. Both s_1^2 and s_2^2 are sample variances, *not* standard deviations.

d. What is the critical value of the test statistic?

$$t = \frac{(\bar{X}_1 - \bar{X}_2) - (\mu_1 - \mu_2)}{s_{\bar{X}_1 - \bar{X}_2}}$$

$$= \frac{(27.3 - \quad) - (\ )}{\quad}$$

$$=$$

$t_{cv} =$

Hint: The H_a is nondirectional and there are 28 degrees of freedom.

e. What is the critical value for the confidence interval?

cv =

CI = Statistic ± (Critical Value)(Standard Errror of the Statistic)

$$CI_{99} = \quad \pm (\quad)(\quad)$$
$$= 5.4 \pm$$
$$= (\quad , \quad)$$

f. What is the conclusion? Explain briefly.

2. Another psychologist believes there is a difference between boys and girls in their learning task persistence, girls being more persistent. For a class of 25 students, the data are as follows:

	Girls	Boys
	$n = 13$	$n = 12$
	$\overline{X} = 26.9$	$\overline{X} = 21.3$
	$\Sigma X = 350$	$\Sigma X = 256$
	$\Sigma X^2 = 9,876$	$\Sigma X^2 = 6,003$

Develop and test the hypothesis at the .01 level of significance. Also construct the 99 per cent confidence interval.

a. What hypothesis is being tested?

$$H_0: \quad =$$
$$H_a:$$

b. What are the hypothesized parameter and the corresponding statistic?

$$\mu_1 - \mu_2 =$$
$$\overline{X}_1 - \overline{X}_2 =$$

c. What is the estimated standard error of the statistic?

$$s_{\overline{X}_1 - \overline{X}_2} = \sqrt{\quad + \quad} \qquad s^2 = \frac{\left[\quad - \frac{(\quad)^2}{13} \right]\left[\quad - \frac{(256)^2}{\quad} \right]}{\quad + \quad -}$$

$$= \qquad\qquad\qquad = \frac{\quad + \quad}{}$$

$$=$$

d. What is the critical value of the test statistic?

$$t = \frac{(\quad - \quad) - ()}{}$$

$$=$$

$$t_{cv} = +$$

Hint: The alternate hypothesis is directional.

e. What is the critical value for the confidence interval?

cv =

$CI_{99} = \quad \pm (\quad)(\quad)$

$\quad = \quad \pm$

$\quad = (\quad , \quad)$

f. What is the conclusion? Explain briefly.

3. Given the following research data, test for a difference between the population means using a nondirectional alternative hypothesis at the .05 level of significance.

Sample 1	Sample 2
$n = 25$	$n = 18$
$\overline{X} = 37.38$	$\overline{X} = 42.31$
$s^2 = 36.40$	$s^2 = 82.15$

a. What hypothesis is being tested?
H_0:
H_a:

b. What are the hypothesized parameter and the corresponding statistic?

c. What is the estimated standard error of the statistic?

$$s_{\overline{X}_1 - \overline{X}_2} = \sqrt{\frac{s_1^2}{n_1} + \frac{s_2^2}{n_2}}$$

$$= \sqrt{\frac{\quad}{\quad} + \frac{\quad}{\quad}}$$

$$= \sqrt{\quad + \quad}$$

$$=$$

d. What is the critical value of the test statistic?

$$t = \frac{(\quad) - ( )}{\quad}$$

$$=$$

$$df = \frac{(s_{\overline{X}_1}^2 + s_{\overline{X}_1}^2)^2}{\dfrac{(s_{\overline{X}_1}^2)^2}{n_1 + 1} + \dfrac{(s_{\overline{X}_2}^2)^2}{n_2 + 1}} - 2$$

$$= \frac{(1.46 + \quad)^2}{\dfrac{(\quad)^2}{\quad} + \dfrac{(\quad)^2}{\quad}} - 2$$

$$= \frac{}{} - 2$$

$$=$$

$$t_{cv} =$$

e. What is the conclusion? Explain briefly.

4. Assume that the psychologist in exercise 1 had decided to use the same group of children in the study, measuring persistence without a parent present and with a parent present. For a random sample of 15 participants, the average duration of effort with no parent present was 20.4 minutes. Later, with one parent present, the average duration of effort was 28.7 minutes. The sum of the differences in the observations with and without a parent present is $\Sigma d = 125$ and the square of the differences, $\Sigma d^2 = 2{,}005$. Using a nondirectional alternate hypothesis, test the hypothesis of no difference at the .02 level of significance. Also construct the 98 percent confidence interval for the magnitude of the difference.

a. What hypothesis is being tested?
   $H_0: \delta =$
   $H_a:$

b. What are the hypothesized parameter and the corresponding statistic?
   $\delta =$
   $\bar{d} =$
   Hint: In this exercise the difference between two means for dependent samples, the difference $(\bar{d})$ is the statistic, and the calculation is similar to using $\bar{X}$ in other exercises.

c. What is the estimated standard error of the statistic?

$$s_{\bar{d}} = \frac{s_d}{\sqrt{n}} \qquad\qquad s_d = \sqrt{\dfrac{\Sigma d^2 - \dfrac{(\Sigma d)^2}{n}}{n - 1}}$$

$$= \frac{}{} \qquad\qquad = \sqrt{\dfrac{\quad - \dfrac{(125)^2}{\quad}}{15 - 1}}$$

$$= \qquad\qquad =$$

$$t = \frac{\bar{d} - \delta}{s_{\bar{d}}}$$

$$= \frac{\rule{3cm}{0.4pt}}{}$$

$$=$$

d. What is the critical value of the test statistic?

$t_{cv} = \pm$

Hint: There are 15 paired observations and $n - 1$ or 14 degrees of freedom. The alternate hypothesis is nondirectional and $\alpha = .02$.

e. What is the critical value for the confidence interval?

$cv =$

$CI_{98} = \quad \pm (\quad)(\quad)$

$\quad = \quad \pm$

$\quad =$

f. What is the conclusion? Explain briefly.

5. A college administrator believes the retention rate to be higher among College Work-Study participants than among other students. Random samples of 300 members each are selected for participation in a two-year study. Over the period, 225 of the College Work-Study participants and 201 of the nonparticipants remain in school. Test the given hypothesis at the .05 level of significance. Also construct the 95 percent confidence interval for the magnitude of the difference.

a. What hypothesis is being tested?

$H_0: P_1 =$

$H_a:$

Hint: In this exercise we are *not* concerned with means, but with rates or percentages of participation for two different groups of students.

b. What are the hypothesized parameter and the corresponding statistic?

$P_1 - \quad =$

$p_1 - p_2 =$

c. What is the estimated standard error of the statistic?

$$s_{p_1-p_2} = \sqrt{pq\left(\frac{1}{n_1} + \frac{1}{n_2}\right)} \qquad p = \frac{f_1 + f_2}{n_1 + n_2}$$

$$= \sqrt{(\quad)(.29)\left(\frac{1}{\quad} + \frac{}{300}\right)} \qquad = \frac{+}{+}$$

$$=$$

$$=$$

$$q = 1 - p$$

$$=$$

$$z = \frac{(p_1 - p_2) - (P_1 - P_2)}{s_{p_1 - p_2}}$$

$$= \frac{(\quad) - (\quad)}{}$$

$$=$$

d. What is the critical value of the test statistic?

$z_{cv} =$
Hint: The alternate hypothesis is directional.

e. What is the critical value for the confidence interval?

$cv =$
Hint: Recall that the confidence interval is symmetric.

$CI_{95} = \qquad \pm (\quad)(\quad)$
$\qquad = \qquad \pm$
$\qquad =$

f. What is the conclusion? Explain briefly.
Hint: Note that the interval does not contain the hypothesized population parameter.

6. Suppose that a teacher education program has a requirement that all students take a course in identifying deficient readers. After their first year of teaching, a random sample of 80 mathematics teachers and 70 science teachers were asked how helpful the required course had been. Forty mathematics teachers and 45 science teachers indicated that the course had been helpful. Is there a difference in the perceptions of helpfulness for the two groups of teachers at the .10 level of significance?

a. What hypothesis is being tested?
$H_0: P_1 =$
$H_a:$

b. What are the hypothesized parameter and corresponding statistic?
$P_1 - \quad =$

$p_1 - \quad = --- \frac{45}{70} =$

c. What is the standard error of the statistic?

$$s_{p_1-p_2} = \sqrt{pq\left(\frac{1}{n_1} + \frac{1}{n_2}\right)}$$

$$p = \frac{+}{+}$$

$$= \sqrt{(\quad)(.433)\left(\frac{1}{\quad} + \frac{1}{\quad}\right)}$$

$$= \frac{}{}$$

$$=$$

$$=$$

$$z = \frac{(0.500 - \quad) - 0}{}$$

$$q =$$

$$= \frac{}{}$$

$$=$$

d. What is the critical value of the test statistic?

$z_{cv} =$

e. What is the critical value for the confidence interval?

cv =

$CI_{90} = \quad \pm (\quad)(\quad)$

$\quad = \quad \pm (0.133)$

$\quad = (\quad , \quad)$

f. What is the conclusion?

7. A psychologist wishes to determine whether teenagers state similar attitudes when interviewed alone and in the presence of peers. Under each situation, 150 youths are asked to indicate whether or not they favor a relaxation of current drug regulations. When interviewed in the presence of peers, 85 members of the group express approval. When interviewed alone, just 70 do likewise. The data are tabulated as shown.

		Alone		
		Favor	Disfavor	
Presence of Peers	Disfavor	2	63	65
	Favor	68	17	85
		70	80	150

Determine, at the .10 level of significance, whether a significant difference exists. Also construct the 90 percent confidence interval for the difference between the two proportions.

a. What hypothesis is being tested?
$H_0: P_1 =$
$H_a: P_1 \neq$

b. What are the hypothesized parameter and the corresponding statistic?
$P_1 - P_2 = 0$
$p_1 - p_2 = 0.566 -$
$=$

c. What is the standard error of the statistic?

$$s_{p_1-p_2} = \sqrt{\frac{a+d}{n}}$$

$$= \sqrt{}$$

$$=$$

$$z = \frac{(0.566 -) - }{}$$

$$=$$

Alternate Computational Formula

$$z = \frac{A - D}{\sqrt{A + D}}$$

$$= \frac{}{\sqrt{}}$$

$$=$$

Hint: Due to the arrangement of the data in the table, the algebraic sign for z is different for the alternate formula.

d. What is the critical value of the test statistic?
$z_{cv} = \pm$

e. What is the critical value for the confidence interval?
$cv =$
$CI_{90} = \pm ()()$
$= \pm$
$= (,)$

f. What is the conclusion?

8. A personnel administrator received numerical ratings of job performance from both employees and their supervisors. An

analysis is conducted to determine whether the consistency is greater in the case of the salaried or nonsalaried employees. Data accumulated for 100-member samples each of salaried and nonsalaried employees yield correlation coefficients of 0.72 and 0.64, respectively. Do these differ significantly at the .05 level? Construct the 95 percent confidence interval for the actual difference.

a. What hypothesis is being tested?
   $H_0: \rho_1 = \rho_2$
   $H_a: \rho_1$

b. What are the hypothesized parameter and the corresponding statistic?
   $\rho_1 - \rho_2 =$
   $r - r =$
   $=$
   $z_{\rho_1} - \quad =$
   $z_{r_1} - \quad = 0.908 -$
   $=$

c. What is the standard error of the statistic?
   $$s_{z_{r_1}-z_{r_2}} = \sqrt{\frac{1}{n_1 - 3} + \frac{1}{n_2 - 3}}$$
   $$= \sqrt{\frac{1}{100 - 3} + \underline{\quad}}$$
   $$=$$

   $$z = \frac{(z_{r_1} - z_{r_2}) - (z_{\rho_1} - z_{\rho_2})}{s_{z_{r_1}-z_{r_2}}}$$
   $$= \frac{(0.908 - \quad) - ( )}{\quad}$$
   $$=$$

d. What is the critical value of the test statistic?
   $z_{cv} = \pm$

e. What is the critical value for the confidence interval?
   $cv =$

$$CI_{95} = \quad \pm (\quad)(0.144)$$
$$= \quad \pm$$
$$= (\quad , \quad)$$
$$= (\quad , \quad)$$

Hint: The confidence interval is constructed using transformed correlation coefficients.

f. What is the conclusion?

9. The director of a statistics department believes there is a relationship between GRE scores and statistics final examination scores. Two graduate level classes of size 37 and 28 have a 0.315 and 0.647 relationship between scores, respectively. At the .10 level of significance, is there a difference between the classes?

   a. What hypothesis is being tested?
   H_0: $\rho_1 =$
   H_a:

   b. What are the hypothesized parameter and corresponding statistic?
   $\rho_1 \quad =$
   $=$
   $=$
   $=$

   c. What is the standard error of the statistic?

   $z = \dfrac{\qquad}{\qquad}$

   $=$

   d. What is the critical value of the test statistic?

   e. What is the critical value for the confidence interval?
   cv $=$
   $CI_{90} = \quad \pm$
   $=$
   $=$
   $=$

   f. What is the conclusion?

10. A family life educator wishes to develop a new inventory of marital adjustment. As an initial step, extensive research is conducted on those inventories already in existence. The following relationships are found for a 150 member sample among scores on inventories A, B, and C:

$$r_{AB} = 0.565, \; r_{AC} = 0.462, \; r_{BC} = 0.631$$

Determine, at the .05 level, whether the relationship between inventories A and B differs significantly from the relationship between inventories A and C.

a. What hypothesis is being tested?

$H_0: \rho_{AB} = \rho_{AC}$

$H_a: \qquad \neq$

b. What are the hypothesized parameter and the corresponding statistic?

$\rho_{AB} - \rho_{AC} =$

$r_{AB} - r_{AC} =$

$\qquad =$

c. What are the test statistic and its underlying distribution?

$$t = \frac{(r_{AB} - r_{AC}) \, \sqrt{(n - 3)(1 + r_{BC})}}{\sqrt{2(1 - r_{AB}^2 - r_{AC}^2 - r_{BC}^2 + 2r_{AB}r_{AC}r_{BC})}}$$

$\qquad =$

$\qquad =$

$\qquad =$

d. What is the critical value of the test statistic?

$t_{cv} =$

e. What is the conclusion?

11. A remedial reading teacher is using two methods to improve student reading ability. Method 1 uses tape recorded instructions with a self-paced text. Method 2 uses a movie projector in a group setting. The teacher is concerned with the difference in the variance in two classes using the two methods. Test the difference at the .10 level of significance.

Method 1	Method 2
$n_1 = 15$	$n_2 = 21$
$\bar{X}_1 = 32.8$	$\bar{X}_2 = 33.0$
$s_1^2 = 80.9$	$s_2^2 = 41.7$

a. What hypothesis is being tested?

$$H_0: \frac{\sigma_1^2}{\sigma_2^2} =$$

$$H_a: \text{———}$$

b. What are the test statistic and its underlying distribution?

$$F = \frac{s_1^2}{s_2^2}$$

$$=$$

$$=$$

c. What are the critical values of the test statistic?
$$F_{cv} =$$
Hint: The tabled F-values are for one-tailed tests at the stated level of significance.

d. What are the critical values for the confidence interval?

$$\frac{1}{F_{df_2 df_1}} \left(\frac{s_1^2}{s_2^2}\right) < \frac{\sigma_1^2}{\sigma_2^2} < F_{df_1 df_2}\left(\frac{s_1^2}{s_2^2}\right)$$

e. What is the conclusion?

12. A researcher wishes to test for a significant difference in the means of two independent samples. As an initial step, it is necessary to determine whether the homogeneity of variance condition is satisfied. Given the following data, make this determination at the .10 level of significance:

Sample A	Sample B
$n = 31$	$n = 66$
$s^2 = 22.50$	$s^2 = 35.30$

Also construct the 90 percent confidence interval for the difference between the population variances.

a. What hypothesis is being tested?
$$H_0:$$
$$H_a:$$

b. What are the test statistic and its underlying distribution?

c. What are the critical values of the test statistic?

d. What are the critical values for the confidence interval?
$CI_{90} =$

e. What is the conclusion?

13. A secondary school administrator believes that the scores of local students vary more substantially on the verbal section than on the mathematics section of a college entrance examination. Using the scores of a 200-member sample, variances of 12,544 and 8,464, and standard deviations of 112 and 92 are found for the verbal and mathematics sections, respectively. The correlation between the two sets of scores is 0.62. Does the research data support or refute, at the .01 level, the administrator's assertion of a significant difference?

a. What hypothesis is being tested?
$H_0: \sigma_1^2 = \sigma_2^2$
$H_a:$

b. What are the hypothesized parameter and the corresponding statistic?
$\sigma_1^2 - \sigma_2^2 =$
$s_1^2 - s_2^2 = 12,544 -$
$=$

c. What are the test statistic and its underlying distribution?
$$t = \frac{s_1^2 - s_2^2}{\sqrt{\frac{4s_1^2 s_2^2}{n-2}(1 - r_{12}^2)}}$$

$= \underline{}$

$= \underline{}$

$= \underline{}$

$=$

d. What are the critical values of the test statistic?

e. What is the conclusion?

Chapter 10 Exercises: Answers

1. a. $H_0: \mu_1 = \mu_2$
$H_a: \mu_1 \neq \mu_2$

   b. $\mu_1 - \mu_2 = 0$
$\bar{X}_1 - \bar{X}_2 = 27.3 - 21.9 = 5.4$

   c. $s_{\bar{X}_1 - \bar{X}_2} = \sqrt{\dfrac{43.6}{15} + \dfrac{43.6}{15}}$

   $= \sqrt{5.81}$

   $= 2.41$

   $s^2 = \dfrac{(15 - 1)(6.4)^2 + (15 - 1)(6.8)^2}{15 + 15 - 2}$

   $= \dfrac{573.44 + 647.36}{28}$

   $= 43.6$

   d. $t = \dfrac{(27.3 - 21.9) - (0)}{2.41}$

   $= 2.24$

   $t_{cv} = \pm 2.763$

   e. $cv = 2.763$
$CI_{99} = 5.4 \pm (2.763)(2.41)$
$= 5.4 \pm 6.66$
$= (-1.26, 12.06)$

   f. Retain the null hypothesis; $p > .01$. The difference between the observed statistic ($\bar{X}_1 - \bar{X}_2 = 5.4$) and the hypothesized parameter ($\mu_1 - \mu_2 = 0$) is not sufficient to discount sampling error. Thus the null hypothesis is retained as tenable at the .01 level of significance. The psychologist can conclude with 99 percent confidence that the interval $(-1.26, 12.06)$ contains the difference between μ_1 and μ_2.
Note: Zero is in the interval.

2. a. $H_0: \mu_1 = \mu_2$
$H_a: \mu_1 > \mu_2$

   b. $\mu_1 - \mu_2 = 0$
$\bar{X}_1 - \bar{X}_2 = 26.9 - 21.3 = 5.6$

c. $s_{\bar{X}_1-\bar{X}_2} = \sqrt{\dfrac{43.26}{13} + \dfrac{43.26}{12}}$

$= 2.63$

$s^2 = \dfrac{\left[9876 - \dfrac{(350)^2}{13}\right]\left[6003 - \dfrac{(256)^2}{12}\right]}{13 + 12 - 2}$

$= \dfrac{453 + 542}{23}$

$= 43.26$

d. $t = \dfrac{(26.9 - 21.3) - (0)}{2.63} = 2.13$

$t_{cv} = +2.500$

e. $cv = 2.807$

$CI_{99} = 5.6 \pm (2.807)(2.63)$

$= 5.6 \pm 7.38$

$= (-1.78, 12.98)$

f. Retain the null hypothesis; $p > .01$. The difference between the observed statistic ($\bar{X}_1 - \bar{X}_2 = 5.6$) and the hypothesized parameter ($\mu_1 - \mu_2 = 0$) is not sufficient to discount sampling error. Thus the null hypothesis is retained at the .01 level of significance. The psychologist can conclude with 99 percent confidence that the interval $(-1.78, 12.98)$ contains the difference between μ_1 and μ_2.

3. a. $H_0: \mu_1 = \mu_2$

$H_a: \mu_1 \neq \mu_2$

b. $\mu_1 - \mu_2 = 0$

$\bar{X}_1 - \bar{X}_2 = 37.38 - 42.31$

$= -4.93$

c. $s_{\bar{X}_1-\bar{X}_2} = \sqrt{\dfrac{36.4}{25} + \dfrac{82.15}{18}}$

$= \sqrt{1.46 + 4.56}$

$= 2.45$

d. $t = \dfrac{(-4.93) - (0)}{2.45} = -2.01$

$$df = \frac{(1.46 + 4.56)^2}{\frac{(1.46)^2}{25} + \frac{(4.56)^2}{18}} - 2$$

$$= \frac{36.24}{0.085 + 1.155} - 2$$

$$= 27.23$$

$$t_{cv} = \pm 1.703$$

e. Reject the null hypothesis; $p < .05$. The difference between the observed statistic ($\bar{X}_1 - \bar{X}_2 = -4.93$) and the hypothesized parameter ($\mu_1 - \mu_2 = 0$) is too great to attribute to sampling error. Thus the null hypothesis is rejected at the .05 level of significance.

4. a. H_0: $\delta = 0$
   H_a: $\delta \neq 0$

b. $\delta = 0$
   $\bar{d} = 20.4 - 28.7$

   $= -8.3$

c. $s_{\bar{d}} = \frac{8.30}{\sqrt{15}}$

   $= 2.14$

   $$s_d = \sqrt{\frac{2005 - \frac{(125)^2}{15}}{15 - 1}}$$

   $= 8.30$

d. $t = \frac{-8.3 - 0}{2.14}$

   $= -3.88$

   $t_{cv} = \pm 2.624$

e. $cv = 2.624$
   $CI_{98} = -8.3 \pm (2.624)(2.14)$
   $= -8.3 \pm 5.62$
   $= (-13.92, -2.68)$

f. Reject the null hypothesis; $p < .02$. The difference between the observed statistic ($\bar{d} = -8.3$) and the hypothesized parameter

($\delta = 0$) is too great to attribute to sampling error. Thus the null hypothesis is rejected at the .02 level of significance. The psychologist can conclude with 98 percent confidence that the interval ($-13.92, -2.68$) contains δ.

Note: The test statistic exceeds the critical value of the test statistic; therefore, the null hypothesis is rejected. The CI_{98} does not include zero, the value of the null hypothesis, which lends support to rejection of the H_0. Note that the values for the statistic and test statistic are negative the way the exercise is set up. To interpret, we would say that study persistence is greater with a parent present.

5. a. $H_0: P_1 = P_2$
   $H_a: P_1 > P_2$

   b. $P_1 - P_2 = 0$

   $$p_1 - p_2 = \frac{225}{300} - \frac{201}{300}$$

   $$= 0.08$$

   c. $s_{p_1-p_2} = \sqrt{(0.71)(0.29)\left(\frac{1}{300} + \frac{1}{300}\right)}$ $\qquad p = \frac{225 + 201}{300 + 300}$

   $$= 0.037 \qquad\qquad\qquad\qquad\qquad = 0.71$$

   $$q = 1 - .71 = 0.29$$

   $$z = \frac{(0.08) - (0)}{0.037}$$

   $$= 2.16$$

   d. $z_{cv} = +1.645$

   e. cv $= 1.96$
   $CI_{95} = 0.08 \pm (1.96)(0.037)$
   $\qquad\quad = 0.08 \pm 0.073$
   $\qquad\quad = (0.007, 0.153)$

   f. Reject the null hypothesis; $p < .05$. The difference between the observed statistic ($p_1 - p_2 = 0.08$) and the hypothesized parameter ($P_1 - P_2 = 0$) is too great to attribute to sampling error. Thus the null hypothesis is rejected at the .05 level of significance. The administrator can conclude with 95 percent confidence that the interval ($0.07, 0.153$) contains the difference between P_1 and P_2.

6. a. $H_0: P_1 = P_2$
   $H_a: P_1 \neq P_2$

   b. $P_1 - P_2 = 0$

   $$p_1 - p_2 = \frac{40}{80} - \frac{45}{70} = -0.143$$

   c. $s_{p_1-p_2} = \sqrt{(0.567)(0.433)\left(\dfrac{1}{80} + \dfrac{1}{70}\right)}$ $p = \dfrac{40 + 45}{80 + 70}$

   $\qquad\quad = 0.081$ $= \dfrac{85}{150}$

   $\qquad\qquad\qquad\qquad\qquad\qquad\qquad\qquad\qquad = 0.567$

   $\qquad\qquad\qquad\qquad\qquad\qquad\qquad\qquad q = 0.433$

   $$z = \frac{(0.500 - 0.643) - 0}{0.081}$$

   $$= \frac{-0.143}{0.081}$$

   $$= -1.765$$

   d. $z_{cv} = \pm 1.645$

   e. $cv = 1.645$
   $CI_{90} = -0.143 \pm (1.645)(0.081)$
   $\qquad\ = -0.143 \pm (0.133)$
   $\qquad\ = (-0.010, -0.276)$

   f. Reject the null hypothesis; $p < .10$. The difference between the observed statistic ($p_1 - p_2 = -0.143$) and the hypothesized parameter ($P_1 - P_2 = 0$) is too great to attribute to sampling error. Thus the null hypothesis is rejected at the .10 level of significance. The science teachers can conclude with 90 percent confidence that the interval $(-0.010, -0.276)$ contains the difference between P_1 and P_2.

7. a. $H_0: P_1 = P_2$
   $H_a: P_1 \neq P_2$

   b. $P_1 - P_2 = 0$
   $p_1 - p_2 = 0.566 - 0.466$
   $\qquad\quad\ = 0.10$

c. $s_{p_1-p_2} = \sqrt{\dfrac{0.013 + 0.113}{150}}$

$= 0.029$

$z = \dfrac{(0.566 - 0.466) - 0}{0.029}$

$= 3.45$

$z = \dfrac{2 - 17}{\sqrt{2 - 17}}$

$= -3.44$

d. $z_{cv} = \pm 1.645$

e. $cv = 1.645$

$CI_{90} = 0.10 \pm (1.645)(0.029)$

$= 0.10 \pm 0.048$

$= (0.052, 0.148)$

f. Reject the null hypothesis; $p < .10$. The difference between the observed statistic ($p_1 - p_2 = 0.10$) and the hypothesized parameter ($P_1 - P_2 = 0$) is too great to attribute to sampling error. Thus the null hypothesis is rejected at the .10 level of significance. The psychologist can conclude with 90 percent confidence that the interval $(0.052, 0.148)$ contains the difference between P_1 and P_2.

8. a. $H_0: \rho_1 = \rho_2$

$H_a: \rho_1 \neq \rho_2$

b. $\rho_1 - \rho_2 = 0$

$r_1 - r_2 = 0.72 - 0.64$

$= 0.08$

$z_{\rho_1} - z_{\rho_2} = 0$

$z_{r_1} - z_{r_2} = 0.908 - 0.758$

$= 0.150$

c. $s_{z_{r_1}-z_{r_2}} = \sqrt{\dfrac{1}{100 - 3} + \dfrac{1}{100 - 3}}$

$= 0.144$

$z = \dfrac{(0.908 - 0.758) - (0)}{0.144}$

$= 1.042$

d. $z_{cv} = \pm 1.96$

e. $cv = 1.96$
$$CI_{95} = 0.15 \pm (1.96)(0.144)$$
$$= 0.15 \pm 0.282$$
$$= (-0.132, 0.432) \; z_r \text{ form}$$
$$= (-0.131, 0.407) \; r \text{ form}$$

f. Retain the null hypothesis; $p > .05$. The difference between the observed statistic $(r_1 - r_2 = 0.08)$ and the hypothesized parameter $(\rho_1 - \rho_2 = 0)$ is not sufficient to discount sampling error. Thus the null hypothesis is retained at the .05 level of significance. The personnel administrator can conclude with 95 percent confidence that the interval $(-0.131, 0.407)$ contains the difference between ρ_1 and ρ_2.

9. a. $H_0: \rho_1 = \rho_2$
$H_a: \rho_1 \neq \rho_2$

b. $\rho_1 - \rho_2 = 0$
$$r_1 - r_2 = 0.315 - 0.647$$
$$= -0.332$$
$$z_{\rho_1} - z_{\rho_2} = 0$$
$$z_{r_1} - z_{r_2} = 0.326 - 0.770$$
$$= -0.444$$

c. $s_{z_{r_1} - z_{r_2}} = \sqrt{\dfrac{1}{37 - 3} + \dfrac{1}{28 - 3}}$
$$= 0.263$$

$$z = \frac{(-0.444) - (0)}{0.263}$$

$$= -1.688$$

d. $z_{cv} = \pm 1.645$

e. $cv = 1.645$
$$CI_{90} = -0.444 \pm (1.645)(0.263)$$
$$= -0.444 \pm 0.433$$
$$= (0.011, 0.877) \; z_r \text{ form}$$
$$= (0.011, 0.705) \; r \text{ form}$$

f. Reject the null hypothesis; $p < .10$. The difference between the observed statistic $(r_1 - r_2 = -0.332)$ and the hypothesized parameter ($\rho_1 - \rho_2 = 0$) is too great to attribute to sampling error. Thus the null hypothesis is rejected at the .10 level of significance. The director can conclude with 90 percent confidence that the interval (0.011, 0.705) contains the difference between ρ_1 and ρ_2.

10. a. H_0: $\rho_{AB} = \rho_{AC}$
H_a: $\rho_{AB} \neq \rho_{AC}$

b. $\rho_{AB} - \rho_{AC} = 0$
$r_{AB} - r_{AC} = 0.565 - 0.462$
$= 0.103$

c. t-distribution

$$t = \frac{(0.565 - 0.462)\sqrt{(150 - 3)(1 + 0.631)}}{\sqrt{2[1 - (0.565)^2 - (0.462)^2 - (0.631)^2 + 2(0.565)(0.462)(0.631)]}}$$

$$= \frac{(0.103)\sqrt{239.76}}{\sqrt{2(1 - 0.319 - 0.213 - 0.398 + 0.329)}}$$

$$= \frac{(0.103)(15.48)}{\sqrt{2(0.399)}}$$

$$= \frac{1.594}{0.893}$$

$$= 1.79$$

d. $t_{cv} = \pm 1.96$

e. Retain the null hypothesis; $p > .05$. The difference between the observed statistic ($r_{AB} - r_{AC} = 0.103$) and the hypothesized parameter ($\rho_{AB} - \rho_{AC} = 0$) is not sufficient to discount sampling error. Thus the null hypothesis is retained at the .05 level of significance.

11. a. H_0: $\dfrac{\sigma_1^2}{\sigma_2^2} = 1$

H_a: $\dfrac{\sigma_1^2}{\sigma_2^2} \neq 1$

b. F-distribution

$$F = \frac{80.9}{41.7} = 1.94$$

c. $F_{cv} = 2.23$

d. $CI_{90} = \dfrac{1}{2.39}\left(\dfrac{80.9}{41.7}\right) < \dfrac{\sigma_1^2}{\sigma_2^2} < 2.23\left(\dfrac{80.9}{41.7}\right)$

$= (0.811) < \dfrac{\sigma_1^2}{\sigma_2^2} < (4.326)$

$= (0.812, 4.326)$

e. Retain the null hypothesis; $p > .10$. The ratio of the sample variances does not depart sufficiently from unity to discount sampling error. Thus the null hypothesis is retained at the .10 level of significance. The teacher can conclude with 90 percent confidence that the interval (0.812, 4.326) contains the ratio of the population variances.

12. a. $H_0: \dfrac{\sigma_1^2}{\sigma_2^2} = 1$

$H_a: \dfrac{\sigma_1^2}{\sigma_2^2} \neq 1$

b. F-distribution

$F = \dfrac{22.50}{35.30}$

$= 0.637$

c. $F_{cv} = \dfrac{1}{1.74} = 0.575$

d. $CI_{90} = \dfrac{1}{1.74}\left(\dfrac{22.50}{35.30}\right) < \dfrac{\sigma_1^2}{\sigma_2^2} < (1.63)\left(\dfrac{22.50}{35.30}\right)$

$= (0.575)(0.637) < \dfrac{\sigma_1^2}{\sigma_2^2} < (1.63)(0.637)$

$= 0.366 < \dfrac{\sigma_1^2}{\sigma_2^2} < 1.038$

$= (0.366, 1.038)$

e. Retain the null hypothesis; $p > .10$. The ratio of the sample variances does not depart sufficiently from unity to discount sampling error. Thus the null hypothesis is retained at the .10 level of significance. The researcher can conclude with 90 percent confidence that the interval (0.366, 1.038) contains the ratio of the population variances.

13. a. $H_0: \sigma_1^2 = \sigma_2^2$
    $H_a: \sigma_1^2 > \sigma_2^2$

b. $\sigma_1^2 - \sigma_2^2 = 0$
    $s_1^2 - s_2^2 = 12{,}544 - 8{,}464 = 4{,}080$

c. t-distribution with 198 degrees of freedom

$$t = \frac{12{,}544 - 8{,}464}{\sqrt{\dfrac{4(12{,}544)(8{,}464)}{200 - 2}[1 - (0.62)^2]}}$$

$$= \frac{4{,}080}{\sqrt{(2{,}144{,}897)(0.6156)}}$$

$$= \frac{4{,}080}{1{,}149}$$

$$= 3.55$$

d. $t_{cv} = +2.33$

e. Reject the null hypothesis; $p < .01$. The difference between the observed sample statistic ($s_1^2 - s_2^2 = 4{,}080$) and the hypothesized parameter ($\sigma_1^2 - \sigma_2^2 = 0$) is too great to attribute to sampling error. Thus the null hypothesis is rejected at the .01 level of significance.

Chapter 10 Mastery Test

1. Assume that the 90 percent confidence interval for the difference $\mu_1 - \mu_2$ does not contain the value $\mu_1 - \mu_2 = 0$. What can be said, if anything, about the retention or rejection of the null hypothesis $H_0: \mu_1 = \mu_2$ at the .10 level of significance? Consider the alternate hypothesis to be nondirectional in nature.

2. Use of the normal distribution as the sampling distribution to test the null hypothesis $H_0: P_1 = P_2$ for two independent samples requires what condition(s) to be met?

3. Use of the normal distribution as the sampling distribution to test the null hypothesis $H_0: P_1 = P_2$ for two dependent samples requires what condition(s) to be met?

4. The confidence interval constructed following a test of the hypothesis $H_0: \sigma_1^2 = \sigma_2^2$ focuses *not* upon the difference $\sigma_1^2 - \sigma_2^2$, but upon what?

5. Assume $s_1^2 = 85$, $s_2^2 = 41$, $n_1 = 35$, $n_2 = 28$. Find the pooled estimate for s^2.

6. Use of the central limit theorem to develop the sampling distribution for a test of the null hypothesis $H_0: \mu_1 = \mu_2$ requires homogeneity of sample variances except under what special condition?

7. The method using the Cochran and Cox and the Welsh procedures must be used to test the null hypothesis $H_0: \mu_1 = \mu_2$ under what circumstances?

8. A test of the null hypothesis $H_0: \mu_1 = \mu_2$ for two small independent samples involves use of how many degrees of freedom to test the critical value of the test statistic?

9. Assume that the null hypothesis $H_0: \sigma_1^2 = \sigma_2^2$ has been retained against the nondirectional alternative at the .05 level of significance. In this case, the 95 percent confidence interval for the ratio σ_1^2/σ_2^2 will contain the value _____.

10. Use of the F-distribution as the sampling distribution to test the null hypothesis $H_0: \sigma_1^2 = \sigma_2^2$ for two independent samples requires what condition(s) to be met?

11. For each of the following, find the critical values of the test statistic.

   a. $H_0: \sigma_1^2 = \sigma_2^2$; $H_a: \sigma_1^2 \neq \sigma_2^2$; 24 and 50 degrees of freedom, respectively; .10 level of significance.

   b. $H_0: \sigma_1^2 = \sigma_2^2$; $H_a: \sigma_1^2 > \sigma_2^2$; 16 and 7 degrees of freedom, respectively; .01 level of significance.

12. Is construction of a confidence interval more common when the null hypothesis has been rejected or retained?

Chapter 10 Mastery Test: Answers

1. If the 90 percent confidence interval does not contain the value $\mu_1 - \mu_2 = 0$, then the null hypothesis has been rejected at the .10 level of significance.

2. $n_1 p_1$ and $n_2 p_2$ (or $n_1 q_1$ and $n_2 q_2$) must be greater than 5.

3. The sum of the frequencies in either of the diagonal cell combinations must be greater than 10.

4. The ratio $\dfrac{\sigma_1^2}{\sigma_2^2}$.

5. $s^2 = \dfrac{(n_1 - 1)s_1^2 + (n_2 - 1)s_2^2}{n_1 + n_2 - 2}$

   $= \dfrac{(34)(85) + (27)(41)}{61}$

   $= 65.52$

6. $n_1 = n_2$

7. $n_1 \neq n_2$ and $\sigma_1^2 \neq \sigma_2^2$

8. $n_1 + n_2 - 2$

9. $\dfrac{\sigma_1^2}{\sigma_2^2} = 1$

10. The distribution of scores for the populations must be normally distributed.

11. a. $F_{cv} = 0.54; 1.74$

    b. $F_{cv} = 6.27$

12. rejected

11 Hypothesis Testing: k-Sample Case Analysis of Variance— One-Way Classification

Comprehension Check

The following summary reviews the material presented in this chapter. To check your understanding of key concepts, supply the missing words indicated by the numbered blanks.

The null hypothesis in analysis of variance, one-way classification (one-way ANOVA) is that the population __(1)__ from which the __(2)__ samples were selected are __(3)__. That is, H_0: __(4)__. The alternative hypothesis is that at least one population mean differs from the rest; H_a: __(5)__ for some i, j. If multiple t-tests are used to test the above null hypothesis by comparing all possible combinations of the k sample means, the Type I __(6)__ rate for the entire set of comparisons __(7)__ dramatically beyond the __(8)__ α-level. However, by using ANOVA to test the null hypothesis, we are able to __(9)__ the Type I error rate at α.

In ANOVA, the total __(10)__ of the scores on the __(11)__ variable is __(12)__ into two sources, the __(13)__ groups variation and the __(14)__ groups variation. The within-groups variation (s_W^2) is defined as the inherent or natural __(15)__ due to individual __(16)__ observed among the subjects in each of the k groups. This variation is attributed to __(17)__ fluctuation and is used to estimate __(18)__ variance or __(19)__ variance, (σ_e^2). The between groups variation (s_B^2) reflects both the variation due to __(20)__ sampling fluctuation and the variation due to __(21)__ treatment effects.

If the null hypothesis is __(22)__, that is, if there is __(23)__ treatment effect, both s_B^2 and s_W^2 would be __(24)__ of the error variance and we would expect the ratio s_B^2/s_W^2 to be approximately __(25)__. However, if the null hypothesis is __(26)__, then we would expect s_B^2 to be larger than s_W^2 and the ratio s_B^2/s_W^2 would be __(27)__ than 1.00.

The actual calculation of the ANOVA begins with partitioning the __(28)__ of __(29)__ deviations around the grand mean (SS_T) into two components: the sum of ____(30)____ groups (SS_W) and the sum of ____(31)____ groups (SS_B). Dividing SS_B and SS_W by the associated degrees of freedom for each gives ____(32)____ estimates for ____(33)____ groups and ____(34)____ groups, called ____(35)____, and denoted MS_B and MS_W. The number of degrees of freedom asscciated with MS_B is ____(36)____ and with MS_W is ____(37)____. The test statistic for ANOVA is the ____(38)____ of the two variance estimates ____(39)____.

The ____(40)____ distribution of the test statistic in ANOVA, the F-ratio, is the F-distribution. The F-distribution is like the ____(41)____ in that it is a family of distributions, each a function of the ____(42)____ of ____(43)____ for the two variance estimates. To test the null hypothesis, the observed ____(44)____ is compared with the critical value of ____(45)____. If F exceeds F_{cv}, we ____(46)____ the null hypothesis and conclude that at least ____(47)____, or a ____(48)____, of the population means differ.

There are several assumptions relevant to ANOVA. These assumptions are that the observations are ____(49)____ and ____(50)____ samples from populations ____(51)____ distributed with ____(52)____ variances. In addition, it is assumed that the dependent variable is measured on at least an ____(53)____ scale. Violations of these assumptions have ____(54)____ affect on ANOVA except in the case of unequal ____(55)____ with unequal ____(56)____ sizes.

Comprehension Check: Answers

1. means
2. k
3. equal
4. $\mu_1 = \mu_2 = \mu_3 = \cdots = \mu_k$
5. $\mu_i \neq \mu_j$
6. error
7. increases
8. a priori
9. maintain
10. variation
11. dependent
12. partitioned
13. within-
14. between-
15. variation
16. differences
17. random sampling
18. population
19. error
20. random
21. differential
22. true
23. no
24. estimates
25. 1.00
26. false
27. greater
28. sum
29. squared
30. squares within
31. squares between
32. variance
33. between
34. within
35. mean squares
36. $k - 1$
37. $N - k$
38. F-ratio
39. MS_B/MS_W
40. underlying
41. t-distribution
42. degrees
43. freedom
44. F-ratio
45. F
46. reject
47. one pair
48. combination

49. random

51. normally

53. interval

55. variances

50. independent

52. equal

54. little

56. sample

Chapter 11 Exercises

1. The director of a regional consortium examined the success of five participating agencies relative to their retention of disadvantaged youths in special 15-week training programs. The following data, obtained from randomly selected samples of program participants, represent the numbers of weeks of meaningful involvement. Set the level of significance at .05.

Agency

A	B	C	D	E
15	6	12	8	15
8	9	14	12	10
6	8	6	9	12
11	7	15	14	11
10	13	9	7	9
4	5	10	10	15

n_j	6	–	–	–	–	$N =$	
T_j	54	–	–	–	–	$T =$	$, \dfrac{T^2}{N} =$
$\bar{X}_j$	9	–	–	–	–		
ΣX_{ij}^2	562	–	–	–	–	$\Sigma\Sigma X_{ij}^2 =$	
$\dfrac{T_j^2}{n_j}$	486	–	–	–	–	$\Sigma \dfrac{T_j^2}{n_j} =$	

Hint: Set up ANOVA problems in the above format.

a. What hypothesis is being tested?

$H_0: \mu_A = \mu_B = \quad = \quad =$

$H_a: \mu_i \neq \quad$ for some i, j

b. What is the value of the test statistic?

$$SS_B = \Sigma \frac{T_j^2}{n_j} - \frac{T^2}{N}$$

$$= 3{,}060 -$$

$$=$$

$$SS_W = \Sigma\Sigma X_{ij}^2 - \Sigma\frac{T_j^2}{n_j}$$

$$= 3,298 -$$

$$=$$

$$SS_T = \Sigma\Sigma X_{ij}^2 - \frac{T^2}{N}$$

$$= \quad -$$

$$=$$

Hint: The calculated value for SS_T should equal the sum of SS_B plus SS_W.

Summary ANOVA

Source	SS	df	MS	F
Between	–	–	–	–
Within	–	–	–	–
Total	298	29		

c. What is the critical value of the test statistic?
$F_{cv} =$
Hint: There are $k - 1$, or 4, degrees of freedom associated with MS_B and $N - k$ or 25 degrees of freedom associated with MS_W.

d. What is the conclusion?

2. A social psychologist wants to investigate the influence that other children in the family may have on the number of child-to-child interactions that kindergarteners make on their first day at school. The data below represent the number of interactions made per child from varying family backgrounds. Set the level of significance at .05.

Number of siblings in family unit

0	1	2	3 or more
4	5	3	4
5	2	5	5
3	0	6	8
2	1	7	3
0	4	5	6
1	3	2	
2	6		

n_j	7	-	-	-	$N =$	
T_j	17	-	-	-	$T =$	$, \dfrac{T^2}{N} =$
$\bar{X}_j$	2.43	-	-	-	$\bar{X} =$	
$\Sigma X_{ij}{}^2$	59	-	-	-	$\Sigma\Sigma X_{ij}{}^2 =$	
$\dfrac{T_j^2}{n_j}$	41.29	-	-	-	$\Sigma\dfrac{T_j^2}{n_j} = 370.16$	

a. What hypothesis is being tested?

H_0: $\mu_0 = \mu_1 = \quad =$

H_a: $\neq$

b. What is the value of the test statistic?

$$SS_B = \Sigma\frac{T_j^2}{n_j} - \frac{T^2}{N}$$

$$= \qquad -$$

$$=$$

$$SS_W = \Sigma\Sigma X_{ij}{}^2 - \Sigma\frac{T_j^2}{n_j}$$

$$= \qquad -$$

$$=$$

$$SS_T = \Sigma\Sigma X_{ij}{}^2 - \frac{T^2}{N}$$

$$= \qquad -$$

$$=$$

Summary ANOVA

Source	SS	df	MS	F
Between	31.60	-	-	-
Within	-	21	-	-
Total	-	24		

c. What is the critical value of the test statistic?

$F_{cv} =$

d. What is the conclusion?

3. A research psychologist compares the effectiveness of two reinforcement schedules in teaching a desired behavior. The following are the numbers of times the behavior is demonstrated within a specified interval following a certain phase of the study. Use analysis of variance procedures to test for a difference between means at the .01 level of significance.

Schedule A	Schedule B
8	6
6	7
5	4
10	7
4	5
7	5
8	10
9	11
12	9
10	8

n_j	–	–	$N =$
T_j	–	–	$T =$ $\quad , \dfrac{T^2}{N} =$
$\bar{X}_j$	–	–	$\bar{X} =$
$\Sigma X_{ij}{}^2$	–	–	$\Sigma\Sigma X_{ij}{}^2 =$
$\dfrac{T_j^2}{n_j}$	–	–	$\Sigma \dfrac{T_j^2}{n_j} =$

a. What hypothesis is being tested?

$H_0\colon \mu_A = \mu_B$

$H_a\colon \mu_A$

b. What is the value of the test statistic?

$SS_B =$

$=$

$=$

$SS_W =$

$=$

$=$

$SS_T =$

$=$

$=$

Summary ANOVA

Source	SS	df	MS	F
Between	-	-	-	-
Within	-	-	-	
Total	-	-		

c. What is the critical value of the test statistic?

d. What is the conclusion?

4. Referring to the data presented in exercise 3, conduct an independent t-test to determine whether or not the two means differ significantly at the .01 level.

Schedule A	Schedule B
8	6
6	7
5	4
10	7
4	5
7	5
8	10
9	11
12	9
10	8
$\bar{X}_A =$	$\bar{X}_B =$
$s_A =$	$s_B =$

a. What hypothesis is being tested?

b. What are the hypothesized parameter and the corresponding statistic?

c. What is the estimated standard error of the statistic?

d. What is the critical value of the test statistic?

e. What is the conclusion?

Chapter 11 Exercises: Answers

1.

	A	B	C	D	E	
n_j	6	6	6	6	6	$N = 30$
T_j	54	48	66	60	72	$T = 300, \dfrac{T^2}{N} = 3{,}000$
$\bar{X}_j$	9	8	11	10	12	
ΣX_{ij}^2	562	424	782	634	896	$\Sigma\Sigma X_{ij}^2 = 3{,}298$
$\dfrac{T_j^2}{n_j}$	486	384	726	600	864	$\Sigma\dfrac{T_j^2}{n_j} = 3{,}060$

a. H_0: $\mu_A = \mu_B = \mu_C = \mu_D = \mu_E$
H_a: $\mu_i \neq \mu_j$ for some i, j

b. $SS_B = 3{,}060 - 3{,}000$
$\quad = 60$
$SS_W = 3{,}298 - 3{,}060$
$\quad = 238$
$SS_T = 3{,}298 - 3{,}000$
$\quad = 298$

Summary ANOVA

Source	SS	df	MS	F
Between	60	4	15	1.58
Within	238	25	9.52	
Total	298	29		

c. $F_{cv} = 2.76$

d. Retain the null hypothesis; $p > .05$.

2.

Number of siblings in family unit

	0	1	2	3 or more	
n_j	7	7	6	5	$N = 25$
T_j	17	21	28	26	$T = 92, \dfrac{T^2}{N} = 338.56$
$\bar{X}_j$	2.43	3	4.67	5.20	$\bar{X} = 3.68$
ΣX_{ij}^2	59	91	148	150	$\Sigma\Sigma X_{ij}^2 = 448$
$\dfrac{T_j^2}{n_j}$	41.29	63	130.67	135.2	$\Sigma\dfrac{T_j^2}{n_j} = 370.16$

a. H_0: $\mu_0 = \mu_1 = \mu_2 = \mu_3$
   H_a: $\mu_i \neq \mu_j$ for some i, j

b. $SS_B = 370.16 - 338.56$
   $\qquad = 31.60$
   $SS_W = 448 - 370.16$
   $\qquad = 77.84$
   $SS_T = 448 - 338.56$
   $\qquad = 109.44$

Summary ANOVA

Source	SS	df	MS	F
Between	31.60	3	10.53	2.84
Within	77.84	21	3.71	
Total	109.44	24		

c. $F_{cv} = 3.07$

d. Retain the null hypothesis; $p > .05$. The conclusion is that there is no difference in the population means.

3.

	A	B	
n_j	10	10	$N = 20$
T_j	79	72	$T = 151, \dfrac{T^2}{N} = 1140.05$
$\overline{X}_j$	7.9	7.2	$\overline{X} = 7.55$
$\sum X_{ij}^2$	679	566	$\sum\sum X_{ij}^2 = 1245.00$
$\dfrac{T_j^2}{n_j}$	624.1	518.4	$\sum \dfrac{T_j^2}{n_j} = 1142.50$

a. H_0: $\mu_A = \mu_B$
   H_a: $\mu_A \neq \mu_B$

b. $SS_B = 1142.50 - 1140.05$
   $\qquad = 2.45$
   $SS_W = 1245 - 1142.50$
   $\qquad = 102.50$
   $SS_T = 1245 - 1140.05$
   $\qquad = 104.95$

Summary ANOVA

Source	SS	df	MS	F
Between	2.45	1	2.45	0.43
Within	102.50	18	5.69	
Total	104.95	19		

c. $F_{cv} = 8.28$

d. Retain the null hypothesis; $p > .01$.

4. a. $H_0: \mu_1 = \mu_2$
      $H_a: \mu_1 \neq \mu_2$

   b. $\mu_1 - \mu_2 = 0$
      $\overline{X}_1 - \overline{X}_2 = 7.9 - 7.2$
      $\qquad\qquad = 0.7$

   c. $s^2 = 5.70$
      $s_{\overline{X}_1 - \overline{X}_2} = 1.07$

   d. $t = 0.66$
      $t_{cv} = 2.878$

   e. Retain the null hypothesis; $p > .01$.

Chapter 11 Mastery Test

1. Find values (a), (b), (c), (d) and (e) for the following table.

Source	SS	df	MS	F
Between	(a)	(b)	(c)	7.00
Within	240	(d)	16	
Total	(e)	19		

2. How many independent variables are considered within a one-way analysis of variance?

3. The independent variable within a one-way analysis of variance may assume how many levels?

4. Assume that the null hypothesis H_0: $\mu_1 = \mu_2 = \mu_3 = \mu_4 = \mu_5$ has been rejected. How many possibilities exist for pairwise differences among population means?

5. For each of the following test situations, find the critical value of F at the .05 level of significance:

   a. Eight levels of the independent variable; eleven subjects in each group.

   b. Five levels of the independent variable; $n_1 = 6$, $n_2 = 9$, $n_3 = 8$, $n_4 = 7$ and $n_5 = 11$.

6. The use of ANOVA procedures requires that the dependent variable be measured on at least what scale?

7. *True* or *false:* In conducting a one-way ANOVA, it is assumed that the within-group variation is of a similar magnitude for all levels of the independent variable.

8. Assume that data are available for eight independent samples, and that *t*-tests are conducted for all possible pairs of means at the .01 level of significance.

   a. How many *t*-tests are conducted?

   b. What is the Type I error rate?

9. Assume the degrees of freedom associated with SS_B and SS_W to be 4 and 65, respectively. If all groups are of equal size, what is the size of each group?

10. Violation of which assumption underlying the use of ANOVA procedures is the most serious?

Chapter 11 Mastery Test: Answers

1. a. $= 448$; b. $= 4$; c. $= 112$; d. $= 15$; e. $= 688$

2. one

3. The independent variable may assume any finite number of levels.

4. 10

5. a. $F_{cv} = 2.12$

   b. $F_{cv} = 2.63$

6. interval scale

7. true

8. a. $\dfrac{8!}{2!\,6!} = 28$

   b. $1 - (1 - 0.01)^{28} = 1 - (0.99)^{28}$
   $$= 1 - .755$$
   $$= 0.245$$

9. 14

10. The homogeneity of variance assumption is most critical. ANOVA is *robust* with respect to a violation of the assumptions except for the case of unequal variances with unequal sample sizes.

12 Multiple Comparison Procedures

Comprehension Check

The following summary reviews the material presented in this chapter. To check your understanding of key concepts, supply the missing words indicated by the numbered blanks.

The null hypothesis in one-way ANOVA states that the k __(1)__ means from which samples were selected are __(2)__ equal. The null hypothesis is __(3)__ if the observed F-ratio exceeds the __(4)__ of F. Rejecting the null hypothesis indicates that at least one __(5)__ differs significantly from another or that a __(6)__ of sample means differs. Post hoc __(7)__ procedures must then be used to determine which of the __(8)__ differ significantly.

Post hoc multiple comparison tests were developed to __(9)__ the Type I error rate at the a priori __(10)__. With these tests, we need to differentiate between the __(11)__ and the __(12)__ Type I error rates. The comparison-wise error rate is defined as __(13)__, the level of significance, for __(14)__ comparison. The __(15)__ error rate (α_E) is the probability of making a Type I error for the set of __(16)__ __(17)__ comparisons. To maintain the experiment-wise error rate at a specified α-level, each comparison can be tested at a __(18)__ α-level or one of the __(19)__ procedures can be used.

Two post hoc multiple comparison tests that are appropriate when group sample sizes are __(20)__ are the __(21)__ and the __(22)__. The Tukey procedure maintains α_E at the a priori α-level by using the studentized range __(23)__ distributions. The Newman-Keuls procedure also uses __(24)__ distributions as the underlying distribution in such a way that the Type I error rate is somewhat __(25)__ than α_E, but it is substantially __(26)__ than the comparison-wise error rate for all possible pair-wise comparisons. If the group sizes are only slightly different, the Tukey and Newman-Keuls procedures can be modified by substituting the __(27)__ n ($\hat{n}$) for n in the __(28)__ of the Q statistic.

If there are large differences in group sample sizes, the recommended procedure is the ___(29)___ method. This method is also recommended for complex comparisons. With the Scheffé procedure, experiment-wise Type I error rate is maintained at the ___(30)___ α-level. In the Scheffé method, each hypothesis is stated in terms of a ___(31)___ combination of ___(32)___ and ___(33)___ that are called ___(34)___. For each hypothesis, the sum of the coefficients must equal ___(35)___. The underlying distribution for the test statistic is the ___(36)___. The critical value of F with the Scheffé method is determined by ___(37)___ the tabled value of F by ___(38)___, which inflates the critical value. The Scheffé method is the most ___(39)___ and, at the same time, the most ___(40)___ post hoc multiple comparison procedure.

Specific sets of hypotheses may be tested by a priori or ___(41)___ comparisons and are performed ___(42)___ of the overall test of the null hypothesis of ANOVA. Two such planned comparison procedures are planned ___(43)___ contrasts and ___(44)___ analysis. The test statistic for both orthogonal contrasts and trend analysis is ___(45)___, and it is computed in the same way as in the Scheffé method. However, the critical value is not ___(46)___ by multiplying by $k - 1$. For two contrasts to be orthogonal, the sum of the coefficients for each contrast must be equal to ___(47)___. In addition, the sum of the ___(48)___ products of the corresponding coefficients for the two contrasts must be ___(49)___. If the contrasts are orthogonal, the hypotheses tested by these contrasts are ___(50)___ and the experiment-wise Type I error rate is maintained at α.

If the independent variable in the ANOVA is ___(51)___, the ___(52)___ relationship between the levels of the independent variable and the dependent variable can be investigated by a ___(53)___ analysis. The purpose of this method is to determine whether the relationship departs significantly from ___(54)___, and if so, whether the trend is ___(55)___, ___(56)___, and so on. Trend analysis is a special case of ___(57)___ contrasts that uses a set of specific coefficients, called ___(58)___ for orthogonal polynomials. The number of possible trends that can be tested is ___(59)___. Tests for trends are made ___(60)___, that is, first for a linear trend, then for a ___(61)___ trend, and so on. If the test for a linear trend is *not* statistically significant, we conclude that the trend ___(62)___ from linearity. More than one ___(63)___ can be statistically significant in a trend analysis.

Comprehension Check: Answers

1. population
2. simultaneously
3. rejected
4. critical value
5. sample mean
6. combination
7. multiple comparison
8. sample means
9. maintain
10. α-level
11. comparison-wise
12. experiment-wise
13. α
14. each

15. experiment-wise
16. all
17. possible
18. smaller
19. post hoc
20. equal
21. Tukey
22. Newman-Keuls
23. (Q)
24. Q
25. greater
26. less
27. harmonic
28. denominator
29. Scheffé
30. a priori
31. linear
32. coefficients
33. means
34. contrasts
35. zero
36. F-distribution
37. multiplying
38. $k - 1$
39. versatile
40. conservative
41. planned
42. instead
43. orthogonal
44. trend
45. F
46. inflated
47. zero
48. cross
49. zero
50. independent
51. quantitative
52. functional
53. trend
54. linearity
55. quadratic
56. cubic
57. orthogonal
58. coefficients
59. $k - 1$
60. sequentially
61. quadratic
62. departs
63. contrast

Chapter 12 Exercises

1. In preparing a planning report, the director of a continuing education program classifies course requests as (1) job-related, (2) consumer-related, (3) health-related, (4) recreational, or (5) other. Over five registration periods, the following numbers of special requests have been received. Use analysis of variance procedures to determine whether or not the given data suggest any differences in overall community interest. Use the .05 level of significance.

Classification

1	2	3	4	5
18	28	23	30	25
25	40	30	35	29
20	26	24	29	22
16	31	25	24	16
11	20	18	22	18

n_j	5	-	-	-	-	$N =$	
T_j	90	-	-	-	-	$T =$	$; \dfrac{T^2}{N} =$
$\overline{X}_j$	18	-	-	-	-	$\overline{X} =$	
ΣX_{ij}^2	1,726	-	-	-	-	$\Sigma\Sigma X_{ij}^2 =$	
$\dfrac{T_j^2}{n_j}$	1,620	-	-	-	-	$\Sigma \dfrac{T_j^2}{n_j} =$	

a. What hypothesis is being tested?

$H_0: \mu_1 = \mu_2 = \quad = \quad =$

$H_a: \mu_i \neq$

b. What is the value of the test statistic?

$$SS_B = \Sigma \frac{T_j^2}{n_j} - \frac{T^2}{N}$$

$$= \quad -$$

$$=$$

$$SS_W = \Sigma\Sigma X_{ij}^2 - \Sigma \frac{T_j^2}{n_j}$$

$$= \quad -$$

$$=$$

$$SS_T = \Sigma\Sigma X_{ij}^2 - \frac{T^2}{N}$$

$$= \quad -$$

$$=$$

Summary ANOVA

Source	SS	df	MS	F
Between	-	-	-	-
Within	-	-	-	
Total	1,016	24		

c. What is the critical value of the test statistic?

$F_{cv} =$

d. What is the conclusion?

2. Referring to the data presented in exercise 1, use the Tukey method

to test for pair-wise differences among the population means at the
.05 level of significance. (Although not required for the Tukey
method, the classification means are ranked from low to high.)

Classification

	1	5	3	4	2
$\bar{X}$	18	22	24	28	29
$\bar{X}_i - \bar{X}_j$		4	6	-	-
			2	-	-
				-	-
					-
$Q = \dfrac{\bar{X}_i - \bar{X}_j}{\sqrt{\dfrac{MS_W}{n}}}$		1.62	2.43	-	-
			0.81	-	-
				-	-
					-

$Q_{cv(.05)}$

a. What is the conclusion?

3. Again referring to the data presented in exercise 1, use the
   Newman-Keuls method to test for pair-wise differences among the
   population means at the .05 level of significance.

Classification

	1	5	3	4	2
$\bar{X}$	18	22	24	28	29
$\bar{X}_i - \bar{X}_j$		-	-	-	-
			-	-	-
				-	-
					-
$Q =$		-	-	-	-
			-	-	-
				-	-
					-
$Q_{cv(.05)}$		-	-	-	-
df $=$			-	-	-
				-	-
					-

*$p < .05$

a. What is the conclusion?

4. A teacher wants to test four different learning environments for a class. Students are randomly assigned to four groups: (1) self-directed, (2) self-directed with weekly conferences, (3) teacher led small group discussions, and (4) student led small group discussions. Some attrition takes place during the year that results in slightly different group sizes. The following are end of the year examination scores. Set the level of significance at .05.

Learning Environment

1	2	3	4
70	69	86	71
80	71	68	78
72	88	81	92
69	66	79	82
73	73	82	90
68	74		85
	70		

n_j	6	–	–	–	$N =$	
T_j	432	–	–	–	$T =$	$; \dfrac{T^2}{N} =$
$\bar{X}_j$	–	–	–	–	$\bar{X} =$	
ΣX_{ij}^2	–	–	–	–	$\Sigma\Sigma X_{ij}^2 =$	
$\dfrac{T_j^2}{n_j}$	–	–	–	–	$\Sigma \dfrac{T_j^2}{n_j} =$	

a. What hypothesis is being tested?

H_0:

H_a:

b. What is the value of the test statistic?

$SS_B =$ —

     $=$

$SS_W =$ —

     $=$

$SS_T =$ —

     $=$

Summary ANOVA

Source	SS	df	MS	F
Between	–	–	–	–
Within	–	–	–	
Total	1,381.96	23		

c. What is the critical value of the test statistic?

d. What is the conclusion?

e. Use the Newman-Keuls method to determine which population
means differ.

	Learning Environment			
	1	2	3	4
$\bar{X}$	72	73	79.2	83
$\bar{X}_i - \bar{X}_j$		–	–	–
			–	–
				–

Hint: An adjustment in n
needs to be made for unequal
group sizes.

$Q =$		–	–	–
			–	–
				–
$Q_{cv(.05)}$ for df $= 20$		–	–	–
			–	–
				–

$^*p < .05$

f. Explain briefly the differences found.

5. Use the data from exercise 4 and the Scheffé method to test for
pair-wise differences among the population means at the .05 level of
significance.

	Learning Environment			
	1	2	3	4
$\bar{X}_j$	72	73	79.2	83
n_j	6	7	5	6
$C_1 =$	–	–	–	–
$C_2 =$	–	–	–	–
$C_3 =$	–	–	–	–
$C_4 =$	–	–	–	–
$C_5 =$	–	–	–	–
$C_6 =$	–	–	–	–

$$F = \frac{(\Sigma C \bar{X})^2}{(MS_W)[\Sigma(C^2/n)]}$$

$$F_1 = \frac{(\quad)^2}{(\quad)\left(-+-\right)} = \frac{}{} =$$

$$F_2 = \frac{(\quad)^2}{(\quad)\left(-+-\right)} = \frac{}{} =$$

$$F_3 = \frac{(\quad)^2}{(\quad)\left(-+-\right)} = \frac{}{} =$$

$$F_4 = \frac{(\quad)^2}{(\quad)\left(-+-\right)} = \frac{}{} =$$

$$F_5 = \frac{(\quad)^2}{(\quad)\left(-+-\right)} = \frac{}{} =$$

$$F_6 = \frac{(\quad)^2}{(\quad)\left(-+-\right)} = \frac{}{} =$$

---

6. A physiologist wants to investigate the effect of different drug dosages on the symptoms of the common cold. Forty people are randomly selected from the population and randomly assigned to four groups. Group 1 is given 1 unit of the drug, Group 2 is given 2 units, Group 3 is given 3 units, and Group 4 is given 4 units. Subjects of this investigation are asked to record the number of days they experience cold symptoms over a three month period. Test the following null hypotheses at the .05 level of significance using the data below.

$H_{0_1}: \mu_1 = \mu_4$
$H_{0_2}: \mu_2 = \mu_3$
$H_{0_3}: \mu_1 + \mu_4 = \mu_2 + \mu_3$

Group	1	2	3	4
$\bar{X}_j$	15	12	7.5	9
n_j	10	10	10	10

C_1: $\mu_1 = \mu_4$ -   -   -   -
C_2: $\mu_2 = \mu_3$ -   -   -   -
C_3: $\mu_1 + \mu_4 = \mu_2 + \mu_3$ -   -   -   -

Summary ANOVA

Source	SS	df	MS	F
Between	331.87	3	110.62	30.06
Within	132.5	36	3.68	
Total	464.37	39		

$$F_1 = \frac{(\quad)^2}{\left(-+-\right)} = \frac{}{} =$$

$$F_2 = \frac{(\quad)^2}{\left(-+-\right)} = \frac{}{} =$$

$$F_3 = \frac{(\quad - \quad - \quad + \quad)^2}{\left(-+-+-+-\right)} = \frac{}{} =$$

$F_{cv(.05)} =$

7. Assume that in exercise 6 the drug dosages measured on a ratio scale and that the dosage increases from group 1 to group 4. Use orthogonal polynomial contrasts to test for linear, quadratic, and cubic trends in the data in exercise 6. Also, graph the results.

Group	1	2	3	4
$\bar{X}_j$	15	12	7.5	9
n_j	10	10	10	10

Coefficients for
Orthogonal Polynomials

Linear	-3	-1	1	3
Quadratic	1	-1	-1	1
Cubic	-1	3	-3	1

$$F_{\text{linear}} = \frac{[(-3)(15) + (\quad)(\quad) + (\quad)(\quad) + (\quad)(\quad)]^2}{3.68\left(\dfrac{9}{10} + \dfrac{1}{10} + \dfrac{1}{10} + \dfrac{9}{10}\right)}$$

$$= \frac{\quad}{\quad} =$$

$$F_{\text{quadratic}} = \underline{\hspace{8cm}}$$

$$= \frac{\quad}{\quad} =$$

$$F_{\text{cubic}} = \underline{\hspace{8cm}}$$

$$= \frac{\quad}{\quad} =$$

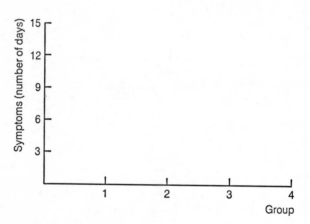

Chapter 12 Exercises: Answers

1.

	Classification					
	1	2	3	4	5	
n_j	5	5	5	5	5	$N = 25$
T_j	90	145	120	140	110	$T = 605; \dfrac{T^2}{N} = 14{,}641$
$\bar{X}_j$	18	29	24	28	22	$\bar{X} = 24.20$
ΣX_{ij}^2	1,726	4,421	2,954	4,026	2,530	$\Sigma\Sigma X_{ij}^2 = 15{,}657$
$\dfrac{T_j^2}{n_j}$	1,620	4,205	2,880	3,920	2,420	$\Sigma\dfrac{T_j^2}{n_j} = 15{,}045$

a. $H_0: \mu_1 = \mu_2 = \mu_3 = \mu_4 = \mu_5$
   $H_a: \mu_i \neq \mu_j$ for some i, j

b. $SS_B = 15{,}045 - 14{,}641$
   $\quad = 404$
   $SS_W = 15{,}657 - 15{,}045$
   $\quad = 612$
   $SS_T = 15{,}657 - 14{,}641$
   $\quad = 1{,}016$

Summary ANOVA

Source	SS	df	MS	F
Between	404	4	101	3.30
Within	612	20	30.6	
Total	1,016	24		

c. $F_{cv} = 2.87$

d. Reject the null hypothesis; $p < .05$.

2.

Classification

	1	5	3	4	2
$\bar{X}$	18	22	24	28	29
$\bar{X}_i - \bar{X}_j$		4	6	10	11
			2	6	7
				4	5
					1
$Q = \dfrac{\bar{X}_i - \bar{X}_j}{\sqrt{\dfrac{30.6}{5}}}$		1.62	2.43	4.04	4.45*
			0.81	2.43	2.83
				1.62	2.02
					0.40

$^*p < .05$; $Q_{cv(.05)} = 4.23$ for df $= 20$

a. The course requests for (1) job-related and (2) consumer-related are different, or $\mu_1 \neq \mu_2$.

3.

	Classification				
	1	5	3	4	2
$\bar{X}$	18	22	24	28	29
$\bar{X}_i - \bar{X}_j$		4	6	10	11
			2	6	7
				4	5
					1
$Q = \dfrac{\bar{X}_i - \bar{X}_j}{2.47}$		1.62	2.43	4.05*	4.45*
			0.81	2.43	2.83
				1.62	2.02
					0.40
$Q_{cv}(.05)$		2.95	3.58	3.96	4.23
$df = 20$			2.95	3.58	3.96
				2.95	3.58
					2.95

*$p < .05$

a. It is concluded that $\mu_1 \neq \mu_2$ and $\mu_1 \neq \mu_4$.

4.

	Learning Environment				
	1	2	3	4	
n_j	6	7	5	6	$N = 24$
T_j	432	511	396	498	$T = 1{,}837;\ \dfrac{T^2}{N} = 140{,}607.04$
$\bar{X}_j$	72	73	79.2	83	$\bar{X} = 76.54$
ΣX_{ij}^2	31,198	37,607	31,546	41,638	$\Sigma\Sigma X_{ij}^2 = 141{,}989$
$\dfrac{T_j^2}{n_j}$	31,104	37,303	31,363.2	41,334	$\Sigma\dfrac{T_j^2}{n_j} = 141{,}104.2$

a. $H_0: \mu_1 = \mu_2 = \mu_3 = \mu_4$
$H_a: \mu_i \neq \mu_j$ for some i, j

b. $SS_B = 141{,}104.2 - 140{,}607.04$
   $= 497.16$
   $SS_W = 141{,}989 - 141{,}104.2$
   $= 884.8$

$$SS_T = 141,989 - 140,607.04$$
$$= 1,381.96$$

Summary ANOVA

Source	SS	df	MS	F
Between	497.16	3	165.72	3.75
Within	884.8	20	44.24	
Total	1,381.96	23		

c. $F_{cv} = 3.10$

d. Reject the null hypothesis; $p < .05$.

e.

Environment	1	2	3	4
$\overline{X}$		72	73	79.2	83

$\overline{X}_i - \overline{X}_j$	1	7.2	11
		6.2	10
			3.8

$$\hat{n} = \frac{4}{\dfrac{1}{6} + \dfrac{1}{7} + \dfrac{1}{5} + \dfrac{1}{6}} \qquad \sqrt{\frac{MS_W}{\hat{n}}} = \sqrt{\frac{44.24}{5.92}}$$

$$= 5.92 \qquad\qquad\qquad = 2.73$$

$Q = \dfrac{\overline{X}_i - \overline{X}_j}{2.73}$	0.37	2.64	4.03*
		2.27	3.66*
			1.39

$Q_{cv}(.05)$	2.95	3.58	3.96
		2.95	3.58
			2.95

*$p < .05$

f. The population mean of group 1 is significantly different from the population mean of group 4; the population mean of group 2 is significantly different from the population mean of group 4. The differences between the other population means is attributed to random sampling fluctuation.

5.   Learning Environment

	1	2	3	4
$\bar{X}_j$	72	73	79.2	83
n_j	6	7	5	6
$C_1 = \mu_1 - \mu_2$	1	−1	0	0
$C_2 = \mu_1 - \mu_3$	1	0	−1	0
$C_3 = \mu_1 - \mu_4$	1	0	0	−1
$C_4 = \mu_2 - \mu_3$	0	1	−1	0
$C_5 = \mu_2 - \mu_4$	0	1	0	−1
$C_6 = \mu_3 - \mu_4$	0	0	1	−1

$$F_1 = \frac{(72 - 73)^2}{(44.24)\left(\frac{1}{6} + \frac{1}{7}\right)} = \frac{1}{13.69} = 0.73$$

$$F_2 = \frac{(72 - 79.2)^2}{(44.24)\left(\frac{1}{6} + \frac{1}{5}\right)} = \frac{51.84}{16.22} = 3.20$$

$$F_3 = \frac{(72 - 83)^2}{(44.24)\left(\frac{1}{6} + \frac{1}{6}\right)} = \frac{121}{14.75} = 8.20$$

$$F_4 = \frac{(73 - 79.2)^2}{(44.24)\left(\frac{1}{7} + \frac{1}{5}\right)} = \frac{38.44}{15.17} = 2.53$$

$$F_5 = \frac{(73 - 83)^2}{(44.24)\left(\frac{1}{7} + \frac{1}{6}\right)} = \frac{100}{13.69} = 7.30$$

$$F_6 = \frac{(79.2 - 83)^2}{(44.24)\left(\frac{1}{5} + \frac{1}{6}\right)} = \frac{14.44}{16.22} = 0.89$$

*$p < .05$ ($F_{cv(.05)} = 9.30$ for df = 3, 20)

We see that none of the contrasts is statistically significant. This result points out the conservative nature of the Scheffé method.

6. Group

	1	2	3	4
C_1:	1	0	0	−1
C_2:	0	1	−1	0
C_3:	1	−1	−1	1

$$F_1 = \frac{(15-9)^2}{3.68\left(\dfrac{1}{10}+\dfrac{1}{10}\right)} = \frac{36}{0.736} = 48.9^*$$

$$F_2 = \frac{(12-7.5)^2}{3.68\left(\dfrac{1}{10}+\dfrac{1}{10}\right)} = \frac{20.25}{0.736} = 27.51^*$$

$$F_3 = \frac{(15-12-7.5+9)^2}{3.68\left(\dfrac{1}{10}+\dfrac{1}{10}+\dfrac{1}{10}+\dfrac{1}{10}\right)} = \frac{20.25}{1.472} = 13.76^*$$

$^*p < .05$; $F_{cv(.05)} = 4.11$ for df $= 1, 36$

7. $$F_{linear} = \frac{[(-3)(15)+(-1)(12)+(1)(7.5)+(3)(9)]^2}{3.68\left(\dfrac{9}{10}+\dfrac{1}{10}+\dfrac{1}{10}+\dfrac{9}{10}\right)}$$

$$= \frac{(-22.5)^2}{7.36} = 68.78$$

$$F_{quadratic} = \frac{[(1)(15)+(-1)(12)+(-1)(7.5)+(1)(9)]^2}{3.68\left(\dfrac{1}{10}+\dfrac{1}{10}+\dfrac{1}{10}+\dfrac{1}{10}\right)}$$

$$= \frac{(4.5)^2}{1.472} = 13.76$$

$$F_{cubic} = \frac{[(-1)(15)+(3)(12)+(-3)(7.5)+(1)(9)]^2}{3.68\left(\dfrac{1}{10}+\dfrac{9}{10}+\dfrac{9}{10}+\dfrac{1}{10}\right)}$$

$$= \frac{(7.5)^2}{7.36} = 7.64$$

$F_{cv(.05)} = 4.11$ for df $= 1, 36$

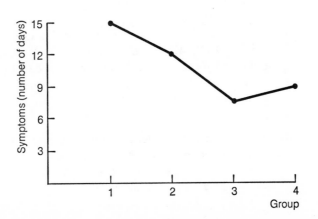

Chapter 12 Mastery Test

1. Assume that the Tukey method is being used, following the rejection of the null hypothesis, to test for pair-wise differences among population means. A harmonic n must be computed due to differences in sample sizes. Find $\hat{n}$, given that $n_1 = 6$, $n_2 = 7$, $n_3 = 8$, $n_4 = 5$, $n_5 = 6$.

2. Which of the three tests—Tukey, Newman-Keuls, or Scheffé—is the most powerful?

3. Which of the three tests—Tukey, Newman-Keuls, or Scheffé—is the *least* powerful?

4. Only the _____ method should be used to test for pair-wise differences if there are large differences in sample sizes.

5. *True* or *false:* Post hoc tests are appropriate only when the null hypothesis has been rejected.

6. For which of the three tests—Tukey, Newman-Keuls, or Scheffé—is the experiment-wise Type I error rate *not* maintained at α?

7. *True* or *false:* For a k-group design, any set of fewer than k contrasts is orthogonal.

8. *True* or *false:* For a k-group design, any set of k or more contrasts is not orthogonal.

9. Assume that the Scheffé method is being used, following rejection of the null hypothesis, to test for pair-wise differences among the population means. If the independent variable **contained** six levels, the critical value of F is obtained by multiplying the appropriate table value by what factor?

10. Assume that independent pair-wise comparisons are being made for a four-group design. If the experiment-wise error rate is to be maintained at .10, each comparison must be conducted at a level of significance no higher than what?

11. *True* or *false:* If two population means are found to be significantly different using the Newman-Keuls method, then the same two are also found to be significantly different using the Tukey method.

Chapter 12 Mastery Test: Answers

1. $\hat{n} = 6.24$

2. Newman-Keuls

3. Scheffé

4. Scheffé

5. true

6. Newman-Keuls

7. false

8. true

9. 5

10. $.10 = 6\alpha$
    $\alpha = .017$

11. false

13   Analysis of Variance— Two-Way Classification

Comprehension Check

The following summary reviews the material presented in this chapter. To check your understanding of key concepts, supply the missing words indicated by the numbered blanks.

The two-way ANOVA is the procedure for testing the ___(1)___ hypothesis when two ___(2)___ variables are considered ___(3)___. This arrangement is called a ___(4)___ design, and it has several advantages. The simultaneous analysis of two independent variables is ___(5)___ since, in essence, we are carrying out two separate research studies concurrently. The two-way ANOVA provides ___(6)___ over more than one ___(7)___ variable or factor. Factorial designs allow us to investigate the ___(8)___ among the independent variables.

The total variation of scores on the ___(9)___ variable can be partitioned into ___(10)___ components. The first component is the ___(11)___ variance (s_W^2), which is variation due to ___(12)___ fluctuation and is considered an estimate of the ___(13)___ variance (σ_e^2). The other components are the variation among ___(14)___ means (s_R^2), the variation among ___(15)___ means (s_C^2), and the variation due to the ___(16)___ between the two independent variables (s_{RC}^2).

In two-way ANOVA the different ___(17)___ effects for the two independent variables in the ___(18)___ and ___(19)___ can be interpreted in the same way as treatment effects in ___(20)___ ANOVA. The ___(21)___ hypotheses for both row and column means state that there is ___(22)___ difference between the respective population ___(23)___. If both of the null hypotheses are true, that is, that the different ___(24)___ effects for the two ___(25)___ variables have no effect on the ___(26)___ variable, we would expect s_R^2 to be equal to ___(27)___ and ___(28)___ to be equal to s_W^2. Thus the ratios s_R^2/s_W^2 and s_C^2/s_W^2 will be approximately equal to ___(29)___. Should there be differential treatment effects associated with the ___(30)___ and/or ___(31)___, s_R^2/s_W^2 and/or s_C^2/s_W^2 would be ___(32)___ than 1.00. The null hypothesis for the interaction is that there is no ___(33)___ among either the ___(34)___ means, the __(35)__ means, or both. If the null hypothesis is false, the ratio s_{RC}^2/s_W^2 will be __(36)__ than 1.00.

In two-way ANOVA we partition the total sum of squares into the four components (1) __(37)__ sum of squares (SS_W), (2) __(38)__ sum of squares (SS_R), (3) __(39)__ sum of squares (SS_C), and (4) __(40)__ sum of squares (SS_{RC}). The variance estimates, called __(41)__ (MS), are obtained by __(42)__ the component sum of squares by the __(43)__ associated with each variance estimate.

In two-way ANOVA, there are __(44)__ null hypotheses to be tested. Tests of the hypotheses on the two independent __(45)__ , the row population __(46)__ and the column population __(47)__ , are referred to as the tests of the __(48)__ of the investigation. The third null hypothesis, referred to as the __(49)__ , is that there are no differences in cell population means that cannot be attributed to the population means of the __(50)__ , __(51)__ , or __(52)__ . The test statistic for each of these hypotheses is the __(53)__ , which is obtained by dividing the respective mean square by the __(54)__ . The underlying distribution is the F-distribution with the __(55)__ degrees of freedom.

The __(56)__ of either of the two __(57)__ variables in two-way ANOVA are __(58)__ if they represent the levels that are of __(59)__ interest to the researcher. If, however, the levels of either independent variable are randomly selected from a __(60)__ of levels, the levels are said to be __(61)__ . If both independent variables have fixed levels, the model for the two-way ANOVA is referred to as a __(62)__ model. If both variables have random levels, the model is a __(63)__ model. If one of the variables has fixed levels and the other has random levels, the model is called a __(64)__ model. Most research in the behavioral sciences usually involves __(65)__ or __(66)__ effects models.

Interpretation of the test of hypotheses for each of the independent __(67)__ is the same as in one-way ANOVA. The hypothesis for interaction is tested in the conventional manner using the __(68)__ ; however, the most effective way to examine interaction is to __(69)__ the __(70)__ means. The scale of the __(71)__ variable is placed on the __(72)__ axis and levels of one __(73)__ variable on the __(74)__ axis. If there is no interaction between the two independent variables, the lines that connect the cell __(75)__ are essentially __(76)__ . A significant interaction is illustrated by __(77)__ lines. An interaction is __(78)__ when the lines do not intersect within the plot, and is __(79)__ when they do intersect.

The assumptions for two-way ANOVA are the same as for one-way ANOVA. That is, the observations must be __(80)__ and __(81)__ samples from populations __(82)__ distributed with __(83)__ variances. In addition, it is assumed that the __(84)__ variable is measured on at least an *interval* scale.

The discussion thus far in this chapter has assumed __(85)__ or proportional numbers of observations in each __(86)__ of the ANOVA matrix. If cell frequencies vary, they are said to be __(87)__ and to analyze the data we can use the __(88)__ analysis. In this analysis, each cell has __(89)__ observation, the cell __(90)__, which is used to determine the __(91)__ of squares and the __(92)__ squares. The mean square within cells is adjusted by multiplying it by the __(93)__ of the __(94)__ n for the cells.

Comprehension Check: Answers

1. null
2. independent
3. simultaneously
4. factorial
5. efficient
6. control
7. independent
8. interaction
9. dependent
10. four
11. within-cell
12. random sampling
13. population
14. row
15. column
16. interaction
17. treatment
18. rows
19. columns
20. one-way
21. null
22. no
23. means
24. treatment
25. independent
26. dependent
27. s_W^2
28. s_C^2
29. 1.00
30. rows
31. columns
32. greater
33. difference
34. row
35. column
36. greater
37. within-cell
38. row
39. column
40. interaction
41. mean squares
42. dividing
43. degrees of freedom
44. three
45. variables
46. means
47. means
48. main effects
49. interaction
50. rows
51. columns
52. both
53. F-ratio
54. MS_W
55. appropriate
56. levels
57. independent
58. fixed
59. specific
60. population
61. random
62. fixed-effects
63. random-effects
64. mixed-effects
65. fixed-
66. mixed-
67. variables
68. F-ratio
69. graph
70. cell
71. dependent
72. vertical
73. independent
74. horizontal
75. means
76. parallel
77. nonparallel
78. ordinal
79. disordinal
80. random
81. independent
82. normally
83. equal
84. dependent
85. equal
86. cell
87. disproportionate
88. unweighted means
89. one
90. mean
91. sum
92. mean
93. reciprocal
94. harmonic

Chapter 13 Exercises

1. The director of a counseling agency asks a random sample of clients to specify their perceptions of counselor effectiveness. Numerical ratings are derived, and these are examined in relationship to (1) age differential between counselor and client, and (2) the counseling approach. Given the following data, use analysis of variance procedures to test for differences among population means at the .01 level of significance.

		Age Differential					
		Younger Client		Same-age Client		Older Client	
Counseling Approach	Directive	22	30	25	28	33	28
		28	25	31	22	30	34
		24	27	23	24	35	32
	Nondirective	36	31	29	31	24	27
		34	35	32	25	28	21
		29	32	26	28	23	25
	Combined	35	30	36	32	33	34
		29	34	35	34	30	28
		32	28	38	36	32	36

		Younger Client	Same-age Client	Older Client	
Counseling Approach	Directive	$T_{11} = 156$ $\bar{X}_{11} = 26.00$ $\Sigma X_i^2 = 4{,}098$	$T_{12} =$ $\bar{X}_{12} =$ $\Sigma X_i^2 =$	$T_{13} =$ $\bar{X}_{13} =$ $\Sigma X_i^2 =$	$T_{1.} = 501$ $\bar{X}_{1.} = 27.83$ $\Sigma X_i^2 = 14{,}235$
	Nondirective	$T_{21} =$ $\bar{X}_{21} =$ $\Sigma X_i^2 =$	$T_{22} =$ $\bar{X}_{22} =$ $\Sigma X_i^2 =$	$T_{23} =$ $\bar{X}_{23} =$ $\Sigma X_i^2 =$	$T_{2.} =$ $\bar{X}_{2.} =$ $\Sigma X_i^2 =$
	Combined	$T_{31} =$ $\bar{X}_{31} =$ $\Sigma X_i^2 =$	$T_{32} =$ $\bar{X}_{32} =$ $\Sigma X_i^2 =$	$T_{33} =$ $\bar{X}_{33} =$ $\Sigma X_i^2 =$	$T_{3.} =$ $\bar{X}_{3.} =$ $\Sigma X_i^2 =$
		$T_{.1} = 541$ $\bar{X}_{.1} = 30.06$ $\Sigma X_i^2 = 16{,}531$	$T_{.2} =$ $\bar{X}_{.2} =$ $\Sigma X_i^2 =$	$T_{.3} =$ $\bar{X}_{.3} =$ $\Sigma X_i^2 =$	$T =$ $\bar{X} =$ $\Sigma\Sigma\Sigma X_{irc}^2 = 48{,}953$

a. What hypothesis is being tested?

$H_{0_1}: \mu_{1.} = \quad =$

$H_{a_1}: \mu_i \neq$

$H_{0_2}: \mu_{.1} = \quad =$

$H_{a_2}:$

$H_{0_3}:$ all $(\mu_{rc} - \mu_{r.} - \mu_{.c} + \mu) = 0$

$H_{a_3}:$

b. What is the value of the test statistic?

$$\Sigma T_{r.}^2 = (501)^2 + (\quad)^2 + (\quad)^2 =$$

$$\Sigma T_{.c}^2 = (541)^2 + (\quad)^2 + (\quad)^2 =$$

$$\Sigma\Sigma T_{rc}^2 = (156)^2 + (\quad)^2 + (\quad)^2 + (\quad)^2 + (\quad)^2 + (\quad)^2 +$$
$$(\quad)^2 + (\quad)^2 + (\quad)^2 =$$

$$SS_R = \frac{1}{nC}\Sigma T_{r.}^2 - \frac{T^2}{N} = \frac{1}{(6)(3)}(\quad) - \frac{(1,609)^2}{54}$$

$$=\quad\quad-$$

$$=$$

$$SS_C = \frac{1}{nR}\Sigma T_{.c}^2 - \frac{T^2}{N} = \frac{1}{(\;)(\;)}(\quad) - \frac{(\quad)^2}{}$$

$$=\quad\quad-$$

$$=$$

$$SS_{RC} = \frac{1}{n}\Sigma\Sigma T_{rc}^2 - \frac{1}{nC}\Sigma T_{r.}^2 - \frac{1}{nR}\Sigma T_{.c}^2 + \frac{T^2}{N}$$

$$= \frac{1}{6}(\quad) - \frac{1}{(6)(3)}(\quad) -$$

$$\frac{1}{(\;)(\;)}(\quad) + \frac{(\quad)^2}{}$$

$$=\quad-\quad-\quad+$$

$$=$$

$$SS_W = \Sigma\Sigma\Sigma X_{irc}^2 - \frac{1}{n}\Sigma\Sigma T_{rc}^2$$

$$= 48,953 - \frac{1}{6}(\quad)$$

$$=\quad-$$

$$=$$

$$SS_T = \Sigma\Sigma\Sigma X_{irc}^2 - \frac{T^2}{N} = \quad - \frac{(\quad)^2}{}$$

$$=\quad-$$

$$=$$

Summary ANOVA

Source	SS	df	MS	F
Rows	264.48	2	132.24	17.49
Columns	–	–	–	–
Interaction	–	–	–	–
Within Cell	–	–	–	
Total	1,010.76	53		

c. What are the critical values of the test statistics?

$F_{R_{cv}} =$

$F_{C_{cv}} =$

$F_{RC_{cv}} =$

d. What is the conclusion?

2. Through the use of a graphic representation of the cell means, determine whether the significant interaction between age differential and counseling approach is ordinal or disordinal in nature. The interaction is _____ in nature.

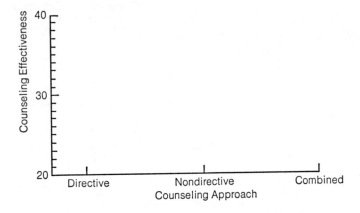

3. Referring to the data presented in exercise 1, use the Tukey method to test for appropriate pair-wise differences.

Counseling Approach

	1	2	3
$\overline{X}$	27.83	28.67	–
$\overline{X}_i - \overline{X}_j$		0.84	–
			–
$Q = \dfrac{}{\sqrt{}}$		1.30	–
			–

$Q_{cv(.01)} =$

Hint: Recall which hypothesis was retained and which hypothesis was rejected.

4. In preparing a report on faculty publications, a college dean examines productivity over the past two years in relationship to (1) academic rank and (2) nonresearch load. Given the following numbers of publications by members of a randomly selected research sample, use analysis of variance procedures to test for differences among population means at the .05 level of significance.

Academic Rank

		Assistant Professor	Associate Professor	Professor
Nonresearch Load	Below Average	6,4	6,4,7	8,6,10,8
	Average	3,5	5,4,8	7,9,5
	Above Average	3,2,4,3	2,4	3,4

		Assistant Professor	Associate Professor	Professor	
Nonresearch Load	Below Average	$T_{11} = 10$ $\overline{X}_{11} = 5.00$ $\Sigma X_i^2 = 52$	$T_{12} =$ $\overline{X}_{12} =$ $\Sigma X_i^2 =$	$T_{13} =$ $\overline{X}_{13} =$ $\Sigma X_i^2 =$	$T_{1.} = 18.67$
	Average	$T_{21} =$ $\overline{X}_{21} =$ $\Sigma X_i^2 =$	$T_{22} =$ $\overline{X}_{22} =$ $\Sigma X_i^2 =$	$T_{23} =$ $\overline{X}_{23} =$ $\Sigma X_i^2 =$	$T_{2.} =$
	Above Average	$T_{31} =$ $\overline{X}_{31} =$ $\Sigma X_i^2 =$	$T_{32} =$ $\overline{X}_{32} =$ $\Sigma X_i^2 =$	$T_{33} =$ $\overline{X}_{33} =$ $\Sigma X_i^2 =$	$T_{3.} =$
		$T_{.1} = 12.00$	$T_{.2} =$	$T_{.3} =$	$T =$

Hint: In an unweighted means analysis, $T_{r.}$ is the sum of row cell means, $T_{.c}$ is the sum of the column cell means and T is the sum of all cell means.

a. What hypotheses are being tested?

$H_{0_1}: \mu_{1.} = \quad =$

$H_{a_1}: \mu_i$

$H_{0_2}: \mu_{.1} = \quad =$

$H_{a_2}: \mu_i$

$H_{0_3}:$

$H_{a_3}:$

b. What is the value of the test statistic?

$$SS_R = \frac{1}{C}\Sigma T_{r.}^2 - \frac{T^2}{RC}$$

$$= \frac{1}{3}[(18.67)^2 + (\quad)^2 + (\quad)^2] - \frac{(\quad)^2}{(\,)(\,)}$$

$$= \frac{1}{3}(348.57 + \quad + \quad) - \frac{\quad}{\quad}$$

$$= \quad - \quad =$$

$$SS_C = \frac{1}{R}\Sigma T_{.c}^2 - \frac{T^2}{RC}$$

$$= \frac{1}{3}[(12.00)^2 + (\quad)^2 + (\quad)^2] - \frac{(\quad)^2}{(\,)(\,)}$$

$$= \frac{1}{3}(144.00 + \quad + \quad) - \frac{\quad}{\quad}$$

$$= \quad - \quad =$$

$$SS_{RC} = \Sigma\Sigma T_{rc}^2 - \frac{1}{C}\Sigma T_{r.}^2 - \frac{1}{R}\Sigma T_{.c}^2 + \frac{T^2}{N}$$

$$= [(5.00)^2 + (\quad)^2 + (\quad)^2 + (\quad)^2 + (\quad)^2$$
$$+ (\quad)^2 + (\quad)^2 + (\quad)^2] - \quad - \quad +$$

$$= \quad - \quad - \quad +$$

$$=$$

$$SS_W = \Sigma\Sigma\Sigma X_{irc}^2 - \Sigma\Sigma\frac{T_{rc}^2}{n_{rc}}$$

$$= 794 - \left[\frac{(10)^2}{2} + \frac{(\quad)^2}{\quad} + \frac{(\quad)^2}{\quad} + \frac{(\,)^2}{\quad} + \frac{(\quad)^2}{\quad} + \frac{(\quad)^2}{\quad}\right.$$

$$\left. + \frac{(\quad)^2}{\quad} + \frac{(\,)^2}{\quad} + \frac{(\,)^2}{\quad}\right]$$

$$= 794 - (\quad + \quad + \quad + \quad + \quad + \quad + \quad + \quad + \quad)$$
$$=$$

Summary ANOVA

Source	SS	df	MS	F	F_{cv}
Rows	15.50	2	7.75	8.42	3.63
Columns	–	–	–	–	–
Interaction	–	–	–	–	–
Within Cells	–	–	–		
Total	62.99	24			

$MS_W =$
$MS'_W =$

c. What is the conclusion?

Chapter 13 Exercises: Answers

1.

Age Differential

		Younger Client	Same-age Client	Older Client	
Counseling Approach	Directive	$T_{11} = 156$ $\bar{X}_{11} = 26.00$ $\Sigma X_i^2 = 4{,}098$	$T_{12} = 153$ $\bar{X}_{12} = 25.50$ $\Sigma X_i^2 = 3{,}959$	$T_{13} = 192$ $\bar{X}_{13} = 32.00$ $\Sigma X_i^2 = 6{,}178$	$T_{1.} = 501$ $\bar{X}_{1.} = 27.83$ $\Sigma X_i^2 = 14{,}235$
	Nondirective	$T_{21} = 197$ $\bar{X}_{21} = 32.83$ $\Sigma X_i^2 = 6{,}503$	$T_{22} = 171$ $\bar{X}_{22} = 28.50$ $\Sigma X_i^2 = 4{,}911$	$T_{23} = 148$ $\bar{X}_{23} = 24.67$ $\Sigma X_i^2 = 3{,}684$	$T_{2.} = 516$ $\bar{X}_{2.} = 28.67$ $\Sigma X_i^2 = 15{,}098$
	Combined	$T_{31} = 188$ $\bar{X}_{31} = 31.33$ $\Sigma X_i^2 = 5{,}930$	$T_{32} = 211$ $\bar{X}_{32} = 35.17$ $\Sigma X_i^2 = 7{,}441$	$T_{33} = 193$ $\bar{X}_{33} = 32.17$ $\Sigma X_i^2 = 6{,}249$	$T_{3.} = 592$ $\bar{X}_{3.} = 32.89$ $\Sigma X_i^2 = 19{,}620$
		$T_{.1} = 541$ $\bar{X}_{.1} = 30.06$ $\Sigma X_i^2 = 16{,}531$	$T_{.2} = 535$ $\bar{X}_{.2} = 29.72$ $\Sigma X_i^2 = 16{,}311$	$T_{.3} = 533$ $\bar{X}_{.3} = 29.61$ $\Sigma X_i^2 = 16{,}111$	$T = 1{,}609$ $\bar{X} = 29.80$ $\Sigma\Sigma\Sigma X_{irc}^2 = 48{,}953$

a. What hypotheses are being tested?

$H_{0_1}: \mu_{1.} = \mu_{2.} = \mu_{3.}$
$H_{a_1}: \mu_i \neq \mu_j$ for some i, j
$H_{0_2}: \mu_{.1} = \mu_{.2} = \mu_{.3}$
$H_{a_2}: \mu_i \neq \mu_j$ for some i, j

H_{0_3}: all $(\mu_{rc} - \mu_{r.} - \mu_{.c} + \mu) = 0$

H_{a_3}: all $(\mu_{rc} - \mu_{r.} - \mu_{.c} + \mu) \neq 0$

b. $\Sigma T_{r.}^2 = (501)^2 + (516)^2 + (592)^2 = 867{,}721$

$\Sigma T_{.c}^2 = (541)^2 + (535)^2 + (533)^2 = 862{,}995$

$\Sigma\Sigma T_{rc}^2 = (156)^2 + (153)^2 + (192)^2 + (197)^2 + (171)^2$

$$+ (148)^2 + (188)^2 + (211)^2 + (193)^2 = 291{,}677$$

$$SS_R = \frac{1}{(6)(3)}(867{,}721) - \frac{(1{,}609)^2}{54}$$

$$= 48{,}206.72 - 47{,}942.24 = 264.48$$

$$SS_C = \frac{1}{(6)(3)}(862{,}995) - \frac{(1{,}609)^2}{54}$$

$$= 47{,}944.17 - 47{,}942.24 = 1.93$$

$$SS_{RC} = \frac{1}{6}(291{,}677) - \frac{1}{(6)(3)}(867{,}721) - \frac{1}{(6)(3)}(862{,}995) + \frac{(1{,}609)^2}{54}$$

$$= 48{,}612.83 - 48{,}206.72 - 47{,}944.17 + 47{,}942.24$$

$$= 404.18$$

$$SS_W = 48{,}953 - \frac{1}{6}(291{,}677)$$

$$= 48{,}953 - 48{,}612.83 = 340.17$$

$$SS_T = 48{,}953 - \frac{(1{,}609)^2}{54}$$

$$= 48{,}953 - 47{,}942.24$$

$$= 1{,}010.76$$

Summary ANOVA

Source	SS	df	MS	F
Rows	264.48	2	132.24	17.49
Columns	1.93	2	0.965	0.13
Interaction	404.18	4	101.045	13.37
Within Cell	340.17	45	7.559	
Total	1,010.76	53		

c. $F_{R_{cv}} = 5.11$

$F_{C_{cv}} = 5.11$

$F_{RC_{cv}} = 3.77$

     d. Null hypothesis 1 and null hypothesis 3 are rejected at the .01 level of significance. Null hypothesis 2 is retained at the .01 level of significance.

2.

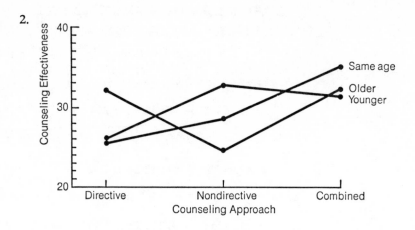

The interaction is disordinal in nature.

3.   Counseling Approach

	1	2	3
$\bar{X}$	27.83	28.67	32.89
$\bar{X}_i - \bar{X}_j$		0.84	5.06
			4.22
$Q = \dfrac{\bar{X}_i - \bar{X}_j}{\sqrt{\dfrac{7.559}{18}}}$		1.30	7.81*
			6.51*

* $p < .01$; $Q_{cv(.01)} = 4.35$ for df $= 45$

The population mean for group 1 differs from the mean of group 3, and the population mean of group 2 differs from the population mean of group 3.

4.

Nonresearch Load		Academic Rank			
		Assistant Professor	Associate Professor	Professor	
	Below Average	$T_{11} = 10$ $\bar{X}_{11} = 5.00$ $\Sigma X_i^2 = 52$	$T_{12} = 17$ $\bar{X}_{12} = 5.67$ $\Sigma X_i^2 = 101$	$T_{13} = 32$ $\bar{X}_{13} = 8.00$ $\Sigma X_i^2 = 264$	$T_{1.} = 18.67$
	Average	$T_{21} = 8$ $\bar{X}_{21} = 4.00$ $\Sigma X_i^2 = 34$	$T_{22} = 17$ $\bar{X}_{22} = 5.67$ $\Sigma X_i^2 = 105$	$T_{23} = 21$ $\bar{X}_{23} = 7.00$ $\Sigma X_i^2 = 155$	$T_{2.} = 16.67$
	Above Average	$T_{31} = 12$ $\bar{X}_{31} = 3.00$ $\Sigma X_i^2 = 38$	$T_{32} = 6$ $\bar{X}_{32} = 3.00$ $\Sigma X_i^2 = 20$	$T_{33} = 7$ $\bar{X}_{33} = 3.50$ $\Sigma X_i^2 = 25$	$T_{3.} = 9.50$
		$T_{.1} = 12.00$	$T_{.2} = 14.34$	$T_{.3} = 18.50$	$T = 44.84$

a. $H_{0_1}: \mu_{1.} = \mu_{2.} = \mu_{3.}$
$H_{a_1}: \mu_i \neq \mu_j$ for some i, j
$H_{0_2}: \mu_{.1} = \mu_{.2} = \mu_{.3}$
$H_{a_2}: \mu_i \neq \mu_j$ for some i, j
$H_{0_3}:$ all $(\mu_{rc} - \mu_{r.} - \mu_{.c} + \mu) = 0$
$H_{a_3}:$ all $(\mu_{rc} - \mu_{r.} - \mu_{.c} + \mu) \neq 0$

b. $SS_R = \dfrac{1}{3}[(18.67)^2 + (16.67)^2 + (9.50)^2] - \dfrac{(44.84)^2}{(3)(3)}$

$\qquad = \dfrac{1}{3}(348.57 + 277.89 + 90.25) - \dfrac{2,010.63}{9}$

$\qquad = 238.90 - 223.40$

$\qquad = 15.50$

$SS_C = \dfrac{1}{3}[(12.00)^2 + (14.34)^2 + (18.50)^2] - \dfrac{(44.84)^2}{(3)(3)}$

$\qquad = \dfrac{1}{3}(144.00 + 205.64 + 342.25) - \dfrac{2,010.63}{9}$

$\qquad = 230.63 - 223.40$

$\qquad = 7.23$

$SS_{RC} = [(5.00)^2 + (5.67)^2 + (8.00)^2 + (4.00)^2 + (5.67)^2 + (7.00)^2$

$\qquad + (3.00)^2 + (3.00)^2 + (3.50)^2] - 238.90 - 230.63 + 223.40$

$\qquad = 248.55 - 238.90 - 230.63 + 223.40$

$\qquad = 2.42$

$$SS_W = 794 - \left[\frac{(10)^2}{2} + \frac{(17)^2}{3} + \frac{(32)^2}{4} + \frac{(8)^2}{2} + \frac{(17)^2}{3} + \frac{(21)^2}{3} \right.$$

$$\left. + \frac{(12)^2}{4} + \frac{(6)^2}{2} + \frac{(7)^2}{2} \right]$$

$$= 794 - (50 + 96.33 + 256 + 32 + 96.33 + 147$$

$$+ 36 + 18 + 24.50)$$

$$= 37.84$$

Summary ANOVA

Source	SS	df	MS	F	F_{cv}
Rows	15.50	2	7.75	8.42	3.63
Columns	7.23	2	3.615	3.93	3.63
Interaction	2.42	4	0.605	0.66	3.01
Within Cell	37.84	16	0.920		
Total	62.99	24			

$$MS_W = \frac{SS_W}{df_W}$$

$$= \frac{37.84}{16}$$

$$= 2.365$$

$$MS_W' = 2.365 \left(\frac{\frac{1}{2} + \frac{1}{3} + \frac{1}{4} + \frac{1}{2} + \frac{1}{3} + \frac{1}{3} + \frac{1}{4} + \frac{1}{2} + \frac{1}{2}}{9} \right)$$

$$= 2.365 \left(\frac{3.50}{9} \right)$$

$$= 0.920$$

c. The null hypotheses H_0: $\mu_{1.} = \mu_{2.} = \mu_{3.}$ and H_0: $\mu_{.1} = \mu_{.2} = \mu_{.3}$ are rejected at the .05 level of significance. The null hypothesis for interaction is retained at the .05 level of significance.

Chapter 13 Mastery Test

1. Find values (a) through (j) for the following table.

Source	SS	df	MS	F
Rows	(a)	4	(b)	6.84
Columns	47.92	(c)	23.96	(d)
Interaction	(e)	(f)	(g)	3.25
Within Cell	(h)	105	5.52	
Total	(i)	(j)		

2. Referring to the data presented in problem 1, find the critical values of F for the main and interaction effects at the .01 level of significance.

3. *True* or *false:* In a two-way ANOVA, it is possible to have a significant interaction without having significance for either main effect.

4. The independent variables within a two-way analysis of variance may assume how many levels?

5. Given the following data, find the specified values.

8	5
4	7
3	4
2	6

10	8
5	9
7	6
3	2

7	5
11	3
9	7
10	4

a. $\overline{X}_{.2} =$

b. $\overline{X}_{21} =$

c. $X_{.312} =$

d. $\overline{X}_{3.} =$

e. $X_{132} =$

f. $\overline{X} =$

6. Is a two-way analysis of variance more powerful or less powerful than a one-way analysis of variance in testing for a significant difference among the levels of an independent variable? In other words, does the addition of a second independent variable enhance or reduce the chances of finding a significant difference?

7. For each of the following graphs, determine whether or not a significant interaction is present between the two independent variables. If significant, determine whether the interaction is ordinal or disordinal in nature.

a.
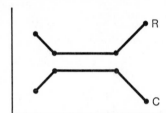

b.
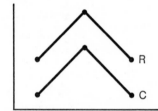

c.
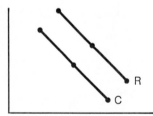

d.

8. *True* or *false:* If the null hypothesis $H_0: \mu_{1.} = \mu_{2.} = \mu_{3.} = \mu_{4.}$ has been retained, then $MS_R \simeq MS_W$.

9. In which of the following cases would an unweighted means analysis be required?

a.

$n_{11} = 8$	$n_{12} = 12$
$n_{21} = 12$	$n_{22} = 18$

b.

$n_{11} = 10$	$n_{12} = 16$
$n_{21} = 6$	$n_{22} = 12$

c.

$n_{11} = 5$	$n_{12} = 5$
$n_{21} = 8$	$n_{22} = 8$

d.

$n_{11} = 15$	$n_{12} = 15$
$n_{21} = 15$	$n_{22} = 15$

Chapter 13 Mastery Test: Answers

1. a. 151.04   f. 8
   b. 37.76   g. 17.94
   c. 2   h. 579.60
   d. 4.34   i. 922.08
   e. 143.52   j. 119

2. $F_{R_{cv}} = 3.50$, $F_{C_{cv}} = 4.81$, $F_{RC_{cv}} = 2.68$

3. true

4. The independent variables may assume any finite number of levels.

5. a. 5.50   d. 7.00
   b. 6.25   e. 5
   c. 4   f. 6.04

6. more powerful

7. a. Significant interaction—ordinal
   b. Nonsignificant interaction
   c. Nonsignificant interaction
   d. Significant interaction—disordinal

8. true

9. b.

14   Selected Nonparametric Tests of Significance

Comprehension Check

The following summary reviews the material presented in this chapter. To check your understanding of key concepts, supply the missing words indicated by the numbered blanks.

The normal distribution, Student's t-distributions, and F-distributions are used to test various hypotheses; these tests are generally referred to as ___(1)___ tests. Since the calculation of the ___(2)___ and ___(3)___ are required to determine the test statistic, the measurement scale of the ___(4)___ variable must be on at least an ___(5)___ scale. For data measured on nominal or ___(6)___ scales, or when the other assumptions necessary for parametric tests are not met, ___(7)___ tests of significance are used.

The one-sample case for ___(8)___ data is called the ___(9)___ test; this test uses ___(10)___ (χ^2) as the test statistic. To calculate the χ^2-value, the observed frequencies are compared to the theoretical or ___(11)___ frequencies. The underlying distribution of the test statistic is χ^2 with ___(12)___ degrees of freedom, where k is the number of ___(13)___ of the nominal variable. As was the case for the parametric tests, if the observed value of χ^2 exceeds χ_{cv}^2, the null hypothesis of no difference between the observed and expected frequencies for the categories, considered collectively, is ___(14)___. A statistically significant χ^2-value does not indicate where the statistical significance lies. However, the individual ___(15)___ can be inspected for those contributing ___(16)___ $(O - E)^2/E$ values to the χ^2-value.

The two-sample and k-sample cases for nominal data are called the χ^2 ___(17)___. When the data can be depicted in a 2×2 contingency table, the test of the significance is the ___(18)___ coefficient. The null hypothesis of no difference between ___(19)___ proportions can be used as well as the χ^2 test of independence. However, for larger ___(20)___ tables, such as a 3×4 table, the χ^2 ___(21)___ is the appropriate procedure.

The null hypothesis for the χ^2 test of independence is that the responses in the categories of the one variable are ___(22)___ of the categories of the second variable. In other words, there is ___(23)___ relationship between the

two variables. To test this hypothesis, the observed ___(24)___ are compared
to the ___(25)___ cell frequencies. The expected cell frequencies for each cell
are determined by multiplying the total ___(26)___ frequency by the total
___(27)___ frequency corresponding to the respective cell, and then dividing
by the ___(28)___ frequency (*n*). The test statistic is ___(29)___ and the appropriate underlying distribution is the ___(30)___ with ___(31)___ degrees of
freedom, where *r* is the ___(32)___ of categories of the variables on the
___(33)___ and *c* is the number of ___(34)___ of the variable on the ___(35)___ .
 If the ___(36)___ hypothesis of independence is rejected, the conclusion is
that there is a ___(37)___ or an association between the two variables. In order
to determine the ___(38)___ of this relationship, it is necessary to compute a
___(39)___ . For 2 × 2 contingency tables, the ___(40)___ coefficient could be
computed. However, for contingency tables larger than 2 × 2, the appropriate correlation coefficient is the ___(41)___ (C). Unlike other correlation
coefficients, the ___(42)___ value of the contingency coefficient is ___(43)___ 1.0.
Thus for each analysis, the maximum value of C ___(44)___ must be computed. Then, to determine the ___(45)___ of the relationship between the two
variables, the ___(46)___ of C is compared to ___(47)___ .
 The two-sample case for dependent samples, when the scale of measurement is nominal, is the ___(48)___ test for significance of ___(49)___ . This
test is used in ___(50)___ designs when the same subjects are measured under
___(51)___ conditions. In this analysis, only those ___(52)___ of the contingency
table that reflect ___(53)___ in opinion in both directions are considered. The
test statistic is ___(54)___ and the underlying ___(55)___ is the χ^2-distribution
with ___(56)___ degree of freedom.
 Two nonparametric tests of significance for the two sample case for
ordinal data are the ___(57)___ test and the ___(58)___ test. The ___(59)___
hypothesis for the median test is that the two populations have a common
___(60)___ . In this test, a 2 × 2 ___(61)___ table is developed in which the
observations for each of the groups are categorized as falling ___(62)___ or
below the ___(63)___ median. The test statistic is ___(64)___ and the ___(65)___
distribution is the χ^2-distribution with ___(66)___ degree(s) of freedom.
 While the Median test is sensitive only to the ___(67)___ of the scores for
the two groups, the ___(68)___ test is sensitive to the central tendency as well
as the ___(69)___ of scores for the two groups. The ___(70)___ hypothesis is
stated in more general terms; there is no difference in the ___(71)___ of scores
for the populations from which the ___(72)___ were selected. In this test, the
scores of the groups that have been measured on an ___(73)___ scale are
___(74)___ and then the ranks are ___(75)___ for each group. The test statistic is
___(76)___ , the ___(77)___ distributions are defined and tables of critical
___(78)___ are available. When the sample size for both groups is greater than
___(79)___ , the sampling ___(80)___ of *U* approaches the ___(81)___ distribution
and the test statistic is z.
 The test of significance for the *k*-sample case for ordinal data is the
___(82)___ One-Way Analysis of Variance. This test is the logical extension of

the Mann-Whitney U-test. The ___(83)___ hypothesis is that the ___(84)___ of scores of the k ___(85)___ from which the samples were selected are simultaneously equal. In this test the scores of the groups are ___(86)___ and then the ranks are ___(87)___ for each group. The test statistic is ___(88)___ and the underlying distribution is the χ^2-distribution with ___(89)___ degrees of freedom.

The two-sample case for dependent samples, when the scale of measurement is ordinal, is the ___(90)___ test. In this test, which can be used in ___(91)___ designs, the ___(92)___ in scores from pretest to posttest are computed and then the ___(93)___ of these differences are ranked disregarding the ___(94)___ of the difference. The test statistic is T, which is the ___(95)___ of the ranks for the less frequent ___(96)___. The ___(97)___ distributions of T are defined and the tables of critical ___(98)___ are available. When the sample size is greater than 25, the sampling ___(99)___ of T is approximately ___(100)___ and the test statistic is ___(101)___.

Comprehension Check: Answers

1. parametric
2. mean
3. variance
4. dependent
5. interval
6. ordinal
7. nonparametric
8. nominal
9. goodness of fit
10. chi-square
11. expected
12. $k - 1$
13. categories
14. rejected
15. cells
16. large
17. test of independence
18. phi
19. independent
20. contingency
21. test of independence
22. independent
23. no
24. cell frequencies
25. expected
26. row
27. column
28. total
29. χ^2
30. χ^2-distribution
31. $(r - 1)(c - 1)$
32. number
33. rows
34. categories
35. columns
36. null
37. relationship
38. magnitude
39. correlation coefficient
40. phi
41. contingency coefficient
42. maximum
43. not
44. (C_{max})
45. magnitude
46. observed value
47. C_{max}
48. McNemar
49. change
50. pretest-posttest
51. both
52. cells
53. changes
54. χ^2

55. distribution
56. one
57. Median
58. Mann-Whitney U
59. null
60. median
61. contingency
62. above
63. common
64. χ^2
65. underlying
66. one
67. central tendency
68. Mann-Whitney U
69. total distribution
70. null
71. distribution
72. samples
73. ordinal
74. ranked
75. summed
76. U
77. underlying
78. values
79. 20
80. distribution
81. normal
82. Kruskal-Wallis
83. null
84. distributions
85. populations
86. ranked
87. summed
88. H
89. $k - 1$
90. Wilcoxon Matched-Pairs Signed-Rank
91. pretest-posttest
92. differences
93. magnitude
94. sign
95. sum
96. sign
97. underlying
98. values
99. distribution
100. normal
101. z

Chapter 14 Exercises

1. A sociologist is interested in the number of children in certain family units and hypothesizes the following proportions: no children—15 percent, one child—24 percent, two children—30 percent, three children—18 percent, four children—8 percent, and more than four children—5 percent. For a random sample of 400 couples, the following results were obtained: no children—42, one child—101, two children—124, three children—72, four children—39, more than four children—22. Test the validity of the sociologist's hypothesis at the .05 level of significance.

   a. What hypothesis is being tested?

   b. What is the value of the test statistic?

Number of children	O	E	$O-E$	$(O-E)^2$	$\dfrac{(O-E)^2}{E}$
0	42	60	−18	324	5.40
1	101	–	–	–	–
2	124	–	–	–	–
3	72	–	–	–	–
4	39	–	–	–	–
5 or more	22	–	–	–	–
Total	400	400	0	–	$- = \chi^2$

c. What is the critical value of the test statistic?

d. What is the conclusion?

2. A college board of trustees requests input from faculty members, students, alumni, and off-campus educators regarding a proposed change of academic policy. The responses from 50-member random samples selected from each of the four groups are summarized in the following table. At the .10 level of significance, test the hypothesis that opinion regarding the change in academic policy is independent of group membership.

a. What hypothesis is being tested?

b. What is the value of the test statistic?

	Favor	Disfavor	Neutral
Faculty members	34 ( )	10 ( )	6 ( )
Students	39 ( )	8 ( )	3 ( )
Alumni	21 ( )	22 ( )	7 ( )
Off-campus educators	28 ( )	18 ( )	4 ( )

O	E	$O-E$	$(O-E)^2$	$\dfrac{(O-E)^2}{E}$
–	–	–	–	–
–	–	–	–	–
–	–	–	–	–
–	–	–	–	–

c. What is the critical value of the test statistic?

d. What is the conclusion?

3. a. Using the χ^2 value obtained in exercise 2, compute the contingency coefficient (C).

$$C = \sqrt{\frac{\chi^2}{n + \chi^2}}$$

$$=$$

$$=$$

b. Estimate the maximum value that this coefficient may assume.

$$C_{max} = \sqrt{\frac{k - 1}{k}}$$

$$=$$

$$=$$

c. Based upon a comparison of C and C_{max}, does the relationship between group status and policy opinion appear to be strong, moderate, or weak?

4. A random sample of 75 parents are asked to give their opinions regarding a proposed program of sex education before and after hearing teachers and administrators discuss the curriculum content. Given the following results, determine at the .10 level of significance whether a change of sentiment occurred.

		Before Discussion	
		Favor	Disfavor
After Discussion	Disfavor	26	15
	Favor	23	11

a. What hypothesis is being tested?

b. What is the value of the test statistic?

$$\chi^2 = \frac{(A - D)^2}{A + D}$$

$$=$$

$$=$$

c. What is the critical value of the test statistic?

$\chi_{cv}^2 =$

d. What is the conclusion?

5. A research psychologist examines the relationship between the classroom behavior of elementary students and their tendency to "keep within the lines" in completing a coloring exercise. The researcher believes that students with satisfactory performance on the exercise will exhibit higher levels of classroom discipline than those who do not. A teacher is asked to provide behavioral ratings for ten students of each type, with such indices assumed to be (at most) ordinal in nature. Given the following data, use first the Median Test and then the Mann-Whitney U Test to determine whether a group difference exists at the .01 level of significance.

Satisfactory Performance	Unsatisfactory Performance
20	17
25	19
26	21
28	22
31	24
36	27
37	29
38	32
40	34
42	35

Median Test

a. What hypothesis is being tested?

H_0:

H_a:

b. What is the value of the test statistic?

$$\text{Median} = \frac{+}{} =$$

	Satisfactory	Unsatisfactory
Above Median		
Below Median		

$$\chi^2 = \frac{n(AD - BC)^2}{(A + B)(C + D)(A + C)(B + D)}$$

$$=$$

$$=$$

$$=$$

c. What is the critical value of the test statistic?

d. What is the conclusion?

Mann-Whitney U-*Test*

e. What hypothesis is being tested?
H_0:
H_a:

f. What is the value of the test statistic?

Satisfactory Performance		Unsatisfactory Performance	
Score	Rank	Score	Rank
20	3	17	1
25	–	19	–
26	–	21	–
28	–	22	–
31	–	24	–
36	–	27	–
37	–	29	–
38	–	32	–
40	–	34	–
42	–	35	–

$$U_1 = n_1 n_2 + \frac{n_1(n_1 + 1)}{2} - R_1$$

$$= (\ )(\ ) + \frac{(\ )(\ )}{} -$$

$$=$$

$$=$$

$$U_2 = n_1 n_2 + \frac{n_2(n_2 + 1)}{2} - R_2$$

$$= (\ )(\ ) + \frac{(\ )(\ )}{} -$$

$$=$$

$$=$$

g. What is the critical value of the test statistic?

$U_{cv} =$

h. What is the conclusion?

6. A counseling psychologist examines the levels of confidence placed by high school students upon their career decisions in view of the major sources of influence upon those decisions. Given the following confidence ratings (assumed to be ordinal in nature) determine if any population differences exist at the .05 level of significance.

Major Source of Influence

Counselor/ Teacher		Parent		Friend		Career Participant		Self-Initiated	
Rating	Rank	Rating	Rank	Rating	Rank	Rating	Rank	Rating	Rank
56	–	59	–	55	–	62	–	68	–
48	–	64	–	43	–	57	–	61	–
65	–	52	–	47	–	54	–	63	–
58	–	49	–			67	–	66	–
51	–	50	–					53	–
60	–								
	$- = R_1$		$- = R_2$		$- = R_3$		$- = R_4$		$- = R_5$

a. What is the value of the test statistic?

$$H = \frac{12}{N(N+1)} \Sigma \frac{R_j^2}{n_j} - 3(N+1)$$

$$H = \frac{}{(\ )} \left[\frac{(\ )^2}{} + \frac{(\ )^2}{} + \frac{(\ )^2}{} + \frac{(\ )^2}{} + \frac{(\ )^2}{} \right] - (\ )$$

$$=$$
$$=$$
$$=$$

b. What is the conclusion?

7. A public school administrator wishes to assess the impact of a compensatory education program upon the classroom participation levels of chronic nonachievers. Two groups of 15 members each are selected for participation. Careful screening makes possible a "matched-pairs" format. The experimental treatment, a ten-week instructional program outside the traditional classroom, is applied to

one of the groups. Three weeks after its initiation, the teacher is asked to specify a participation index (assumed to be measured on an ordinal scale) for each of the students. Given the following data, use the Wilcoxon Matched-Pairs Signed-Rank test to determine whether a difference exists between the experimental and control groups at the .01 level of significance. Use a directional alternative hypothesis.

Matched-Pair	Experimental Group	Control Group	Difference	Rank of Difference	Rank with Less Frequent Sign
1	18	14	4	6.5	
2	15	6	9	12	
3	20	10	10	–	
4	12	12	–	–	
5	15	16	–	–	
6	16	8	–	–	
7	18	12	–	–	
8	22	19	–	–	
9	14	4	–	–	
10	17	10	–	–	
11	9	13	–	–	
12	12	15	–	–	
13	21	16	–	–	
14	19	5	–	–	
15	10	12	–	–	
					$T =$

a. What are the value of the test statistic and the critical value of the test statistic?

$T_{cv} =$

b. What is the conclusion?

Chapter 14 Exercises: Answers

1. a. The observed frequencies equal the expected frequencies.

b.

Number of children	O	E	$O-E$	$(O-E)^2$	$\dfrac{(O-E)^2}{E}$
0	42	60	−18	324	5.40
1	101	96	5	25	0.26
2	124	120	4	16	0.13
3	72	72	0	0	0.00
4	39	32	7	49	1.53
5 or more	22	20	2	4	0.20
Total	400	400	0	–	$7.52 = \chi^2$

c. The critical value of χ^2 at the .05 level of significance is 11.07.

d. The null hypothesis of equality between the observed and expected frequencies is retained at the .05 level of significance.

2. a. The opinion on the change of academic policy is independent of group membership.

b.

	Favor	Disfavor	Neutral	
Faculty members	34 (30.5)	10 (14.5)	6 (5.0)	50
Students	39 (30.5)	8 (14.5)	3 (5.0)	50
Alumni	21 (30.5)	22 (14.5)	7 (5.0)	50
Off-campus educators	28 (30.5)	18 (14.5)	4 (5.0)	50
	122	58	20	200

O	E	$O-E$	$(O-E)^2$	$\dfrac{(O-E)^2}{E}$
34	30.5	3.5	12.25	0.40
39	30.5	8.5	72.25	2.37
21	30.5	−9.5	90.25	2.96
28	30.5	−2.5	6.25	0.20
10	14.5	−4.5	20.25	1.40
8	14.5	−6.5	42.25	2.91
22	14.5	7.5	56.25	3.88
18	14.5	3.5	12.25	0.84
6	5.0	1.0	1.00	0.20
3	5.0	−2.0	4.00	0.80
7	5.0	2.0	4.00	0.80
4	5.0	−1.0	1.00	0.20
200	200	0	–	$16.96 = \chi^2$

c. The critical value of χ^2 at the .10 level of significance is 10.64.

d. The null hypothesis of independence between opinion and group status is rejected at the .10 level of significance. The major contributors to the χ^2 value are students, who are most strongly in favor of the proposed change of policy, and alumni, who are most strongly opposed.

3. a. $C = \sqrt{\dfrac{16.96}{200 + 16.96}}$

$= 0.280$

b. $C_{max} = \sqrt{\dfrac{3 - 1}{3}}$

$= 0.816$

c. weak (low positive correlation)

4. a. There is no difference in parent opinion before and after the discussion.

b. $\chi^2 = \dfrac{(26 - 11)^2}{26 + 11}$

$= \dfrac{225}{37}$

$= 6.08$

c. $\chi_{cv}^2 = 2.71$

d. The null hypothesis of no change of sentiment is rejected at the .10 level of significance.

5. a. $H_0\text{: Mdn}_1 = \text{Mdn}_2$
   $H_a\text{: Mdn}_1 > \text{Mdn}_2$

b. Median $= \dfrac{28 + 29}{2} = 28.5$

	Satisfactory	Unsatisfactory
Above Median	6	4
Below Median	4	6

$$\chi^2 = \frac{20[(6)(6) - (4)(4)]^2}{(6 + 4)(4 + 6)(6 + 4)(4 + 6)}$$

$$= \frac{8{,}000}{10{,}000}$$

$$= 0.80$$

c. The critical value of χ^2, for a one-tailed test at the .01 level of significance is 5.41.

d. The null hypothesis of no difference between the two groups is retained at the .01 level of significance.

e. H_0: Behavior$_1$ = Behavior$_2$
H_a: Behavior$_1$ > Behavior$_2$

f.

Satisfactory Performance		Unsatisfactory Performance	
Score	Rank	Score	Rank
20	3	17	1
25	7	19	2
26	8	21	4
28	10	22	5
31	12	24	6
36	16	27	9
37	17	29	11
38	18	32	13
40	19	34	14
42	20	35	15
	130 = R_1		80 = R_2

$$U_1 = (10)(10) + \frac{(10)(11)}{2} - 130$$
$$= 100 + 55 - 130$$
$$= 25$$

$$U_2 = (10)(10) + \frac{(10)(11)}{2} - 80$$
$$= 100 + 55 - 80$$
$$= 75$$
Therefore, $U = 25$

g. $U_{cv} = 20$

h. Retain the null hypothesis.

6.   Major Source of Influence

Counselor/ Teacher		Parent		Friend		Career Participant		Self-Initiated	
Rating	Rank	Rating	Rank	Rating	Rank	Rating	Rank	Rating	Rank
56	11	59	14	55	10	62	17	68	23
48	3	64	19	43	1	57	12	61	16
65	20	52	7	47	2	54	9	63	18
58	13	49	4			67	22	66	21
51	6	50	5					53	8
60	15								
	$68 = R_1$		$49 = R_2$		$13 = R_3$		$60 = R_4$		$86 = R_5$

a. $H = \dfrac{12}{23(24)} \left[\dfrac{(68)^2}{6} + \dfrac{(49)^2}{5} + \dfrac{(13)^2}{3} + \dfrac{(60)^2}{4} + \dfrac{(86)^2}{5} \right] - 3(24)$

$= \dfrac{12}{552}(770.67 + 480.2 + 56.33 + 900.0 + 1{,}479.2) - 72$

$= 8.14$

b. The critical value of H at the .05 level of significance is 9.49. Therefore, the null hypothesis of no population differences is retained at the .05 level of significance.

7. Matched- Pair	Experimental Group	Control Group	Differ- ence	Rank of Difference	Rank with Less Frequent Sign
1	18	14	4	6.5	
2	15	6	9	12	
3	20	10	10	13.5	
4	12	12	0	1	
5	15	16	−1	−2	2
6	16	8	8	11	
7	18	12	6	9	
8	22	19	3	4.5	
9	14	4	10	13.5	
10	17	10	7	10	
11	9	13	−4	−6.5	6.5
12	12	15	−3	−4.5	4.5
13	21	16	5	8	
14	19	5	14	15	
15	10	12	−2	−3	3
					$T = 16$

    a. $T_{cv} = 20$

    b. Since the derived value of T is *less than* the critical value, the null hypothesis of no difference between the experimental and control groups is rejected at the .01 level of significance.

Chapter 14 Mastery Test

1. *True* or *false:* The χ^2 sampling distribution becomes more positively skewed as the number of degrees of freedom increases.

2. *True* or *false:* The maximum value of the contingency coefficient (C) increases as additional categories are assigned to the independent variables.

3. Assume that df $= 42$ and $\chi^2 = 62.56$. Using the normal distribution as the underlying distribution, find the value of the test statistic and examine its significance at the .05 level.

4. Assume that a significant difference has been found at the .05 level using the Median Test. What, if anything, can be said about the existence of a similar significant difference using the Mann-Whitney U-Test?

5. Given that a contingency table contains six rows and four columns, what number of degrees of freedom is used to determine the critical value of the χ^2 statistic?

6. Find the expected frequencies within each of the twelve cells, given the specified observed frequencies.

Columns

6	10	9	8
5	15	3	6
10	12	7	9

Rows

7. The χ^2 test of independence, in the case of a larger than 2×2 contingency table, is appropriate only under what condition(s)?

8. *True* or *false:* The value of the contingency coefficient (C) is always greater than, or equal to zero.

Chapter 14 Mastery Test: Answers

1. false

2. true

3. 2.08. The test statistic is significant at the .05 level.

4. A significant difference will also be found in this case, since the Mann-Whitney U-Test is *more* powerful than the Median Test.

5. 15

6.

		Columns		
	6.93	12.21	6.27	7.59
Rows	6.09	10.73	5.51	6.67
	7.98	14.06	7.22	8.74

7. Fewer than twenty percent of the cells should have expected frequencies less than 5, and no expected frequency should be less than 1.

8. true

15

Linear Regression: Prediction and Estimation

Comprehension Check

The following summary reviews the material presented in this chapter. To check your understanding of key concepts, supply the missing words indicated by the numbered blanks.

The concept of linear regression involves predicting or ___(1)___ a ___(2)___ on one variable based upon ___(3)___ of a score on another variable. In linear regression, the slope-intercept equation of a straight line is $\widehat{Y} = bX + a$, where $\widehat{Y}$ is the ___(4)___ score, b is the ___(5)___ of the line, and a is the Y ___(6)___. The slope is defined as the change in ___(7)___ for a one-unit increase in ___(8)___.

In predicting Y from X, the slope of the regression line is denoted ___(9)___ and is referred to as the regression ___(10)___. The intercept is denoted ___(11)___ and is called the regression ___(12)___. Thus the regression equation for predicting Y from X is given by ___(13)___. This particular regression equation reflects the ___(14)___ line that best fits the ___(15)___ of data points. This line is ___(16)___ to the data points by what is called the method of ___(17)___, which requires that $\Sigma (Y - \widehat{Y})^2$ be a ___(18)___.

It is also possible to develop a regression equation to predict X from Y; this regression equation is given by $\widehat{X} = b_{x.y}Y + a_{x.y}$. However, in behavioral science research, the conventional regression procedure is to predict the value of ___(19)___ based upon knowledge of ___(20)___.

The difference between an individual's actual score and predicted score is defined as the ___(21)___ in prediction. In linear regression, we are concerned with the distribution of ___(22)___ scores and the variance and ___(23)___ of these scores. The mean of this distribution of error scores is ___(24)___. The estimated standard deviation of the error scores is called the ___(25)___ error of ___(26)___.

Assumptions associated with the development of the regression line are that the Y and X variables are ___(27)___, that variables are measured on at least the ___(28)___ scale, and that variables have a ___(29)___ relationship. The errors in prediction (e_i) are normally distributed with a ___(30)___ equal to zero and a ___(31)___ equal to $\sigma_{y.x}{}^2$. The assumption of ___(32)___ is that the variance of the errors of prediction at every X value is the ___(33)___ .

The total variance of Y can be partitioned into the variance of the ___(34)___ scores and the variance of the ___(35)___ of ___(36)___ . The ratio of the variance of the predicted scores to the total variance of Y equals ___(37)___ , the coefficient of ___(38)___ . This coefficient is the proportion of the ___(39)___ of Y that is ___(40)___ by knowledge of the ___(41)___ variable.

Comprehension Check: Answers

1. estimating
4. predicted
7. Y
10. coefficient
13. $\widehat{Y} = b_{y.x}X + a_{y.x}$
16. fit
19. Y
22. error
25. standard
28. interval
31. variance
34. predicted
37. r^2
40. explained

2. score
5. slope
8. X
11. $a_{y.x}$
14. straight
17. least squares
20. X
23. standard deviation
26. prediction
29. linear
32. homoscedasticity
35. errors
38. determination
41. X

3. knowledge
6. intercept
9. $b_{y.x}$
12. constant
15. scattergram
18. minimum
21. error
24. zero
27. continuous
30. mean
33. same
36. prediction
39. variance

Chapter 15 Exercises

1. A professional licensing examination contains both written and clinical components. The following scores are available for a 15-member random sample of recent examinees. Complete the table.

Examinee	Written (X)	Clinical (Y)	X^2	Y^2	XY
1	85	89	7,225	7,921	7,565
2	76	71	5,776	5,041	5,396
3	92	90	8,464	8,100	8,280
4	60	53	–	–	–
5	81	88	–	–	–
6	84	85	–	–	–
7	95	98	–	–	–
8	56	62	–	–	–
9	76	79	–	–	–
10	68	62	–	–	–
11	93	92	–	–	–
12	71	75	–	–	–
13	88	90	–	–	–
14	69	78	–	–	–
15	80	91			
Σ	1,174				

2. Complete the table for the following sets of scores.

Participant	X	Y	X^2	Y^2	XY
1	4	6	16	36	24
2	6	5	–	–	–
3	10	9	–	–	–
4	8	8	–	–	–
5	12	10	–	–	–
6	8	11	–	–	–
7	5	8	–	–	–
8	3	4	–	–	–
9	10	7	–	–	–
10	7	6	–	–	–
Σ					

a. Compute the regression equation.

$$b_{y.x} = \frac{n\Sigma XY - \Sigma X \Sigma Y}{n\Sigma X^2 - (\Sigma X)^2} =$$

$$a_{y.x} = \frac{\Sigma Y - b_{y.x}\Sigma X}{n} =$$

$$\hat{Y} = b_{y.x}X + a_{y.x} =$$

$$b_{x.y} = \frac{n\Sigma XY - \Sigma X \Sigma Y}{n\Sigma Y^2 - (\Sigma Y)^2} =$$

$$a_{x.y} = \frac{\Sigma X - b_{x.y}\Sigma Y}{n} =$$

$$\hat{X} = b_{x.y}Y + a_{x.y} =$$

b. Plot the two regression lines from the data above.

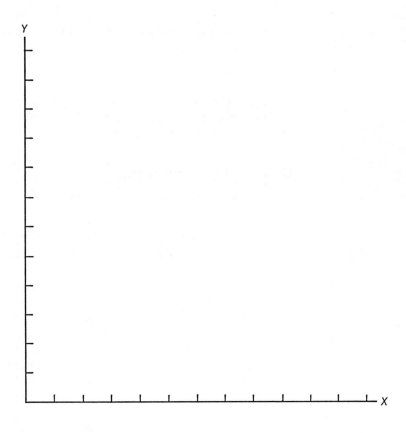

3. Using the data in exercise 2, find the standard error $s_{y \cdot x}$.

Participant	X	Y	$\widehat{Y}$	$e = Y - \widehat{Y}$	e^2
1	4	6	5.62	0.38	0.14
2	6	5	–	–	–
3	10	9	–	–	–
4	8	8	–	–	–
5	12	10	–	–	–
6	8	11	–	–	–
7	5	8	–	–	–
8	3	4	–	–	–
9	10	7	–	–	–
10	7	6	–	–	–
				0	

$s_{y \cdot x} =$

4. Determine the correlation coefficient r for the sets of scores in exercise 2.

$r =$

5. Given the regression equation $\widehat{Y} = 0.42X + 7.25$, find the 90 percent confidence interval for the value of Y corresponding to an X-score of 62. Assume that $s_{y \cdot x} = 4.07$.

Chapter 15 Exercises: Answers

1.

Examinee	Written (X)	Clinical (Y)	X^2	Y^2	XY
1	85	89	7,225	7,921	7,565
2	76	71	5,776	5,041	5,396
3	92	90	8,464	8,100	8,280
4	60	53	3,600	2,809	3,180
5	81	88	6,561	7,744	7,128
6	84	85	7,056	7,225	7,140
7	95	98	9,025	9,604	9,310
8	56	62	3,136	3,844	3,472
9	76	79	5,776	6,241	6,004
10	68	62	4,624	3,844	4,216
11	93	92	8,649	8,464	8,556
12	71	75	5,041	5,625	5,325
13	88	90	7,744	8,100	7,920
14	69	78	4,761	6,084	5,382
15	80	91	6,400	8,281	7,280
Σ	1,174	1,203	93,838	98,927	96,154

2.

Participant	X	Y	X^2	Y^2	XY
1	4	6	16	36	24
2	6	5	36	25	30
3	10	9	100	81	90
4	8	8	64	64	64
5	12	10	144	100	120
6	8	11	64	121	88
7	5	8	25	64	40
8	3	4	9	16	12
9	10	7	100	49	70
10	7	6	49	36	42
Σ	73	74	607	592	580

a.
$$b_{y.x} = \frac{10(580) - (73)(74)}{10(607) - (73)^2}$$

$$= \frac{5800 - 5402}{6070 - 5329}$$

$$= \frac{398}{741}$$

$$= 0.537$$

$$a_{y.x} = \frac{74 - (0.537)(73)}{10}$$

$$= \frac{74 - 39.201}{10}$$

$$= \frac{34.799}{10}$$

$$= 3.48$$

$$\widehat{Y} = 0.537X + 3.48$$

$$b_{x.y} = \frac{10(580) - (73)(74)}{10(592) - (74)^2}$$

$$= \frac{5800 - 5402}{5920 - 5476}$$

$$= \frac{398}{444}$$

$$= 0.896$$

$$a_{x.y} = \frac{73 - 0.896(74)}{10}$$

$$= \frac{73 - 66.304}{10}$$

$$= \frac{6.696}{10}$$

$$= 0.67$$

$$\widehat{X} = 0.896Y + 0.67$$

b.

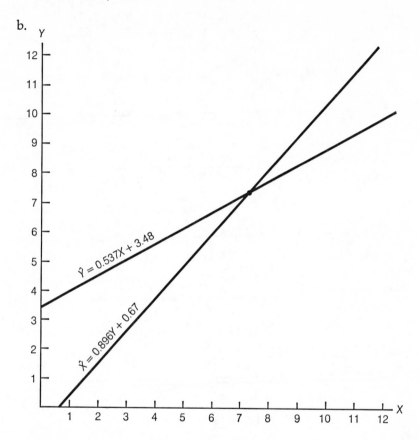

3.

Participant	X	Y	$\widehat{Y}$	$e = Y - \widehat{Y}$	e^2
1	4	6	5.62	0.38	0.14
2	6	5	6.70	−1.70	2.89
3	10	9	8.85	0.15	0.02
4	8	8	7.78	0.22	0.05
5	12	10	9.92	0.08	0.01
6	8	11	7.78	3.22	10.37
7	5	8	6.17	1.83	3.35
8	3	4	5.09	−1.09	1.19
9	10	7	8.85	−1.85	3.42
10	7	6	7.24	−1.24	1.54
				0	22.98

$$s_{y.x} = \sqrt{\frac{\Sigma e^2}{n-2}}$$

$$= \sqrt{\frac{22.98}{10-2}}$$

$$= 1.69$$

4. $r^2 = b_{y.x}b_{x.y}$

$r = \sqrt{(0.537)(0.896)}$

$\quad = \sqrt{0.481}$

$\quad = 0.69$

5. $\hat{Y} = 0.42(62) + 7.25$

$\quad = 26.04 + 7.25$

$\quad = 33.29$

$\text{CI}_{90} = 33.29 \pm (1.645)(4.07)$

$\quad\quad = (26.59, 39.99)$

Chapter 15 Mastery Test

1. Assume that $r = 0.63$ and $s_y = 2.34$. Find $s_{y.x}$.

2. *True* or *false*: $b_{x.y}$ is a coefficient used to predict a value of Y for a given value of X.

3. The line $Y = 4X + 5$ intercepts the Y-axis at what point?

4. *True* or *false*: If an X-score is used to predict a Y-score, and that score is then used to predict another X-score, the original score will be acquired.

5. *True* or *false*: If $s_{y.x} = 0$, then $s_{x.y} = 0$.

6. $s_{y.x} = 0$ if and only if r is equal to what value(s)?

7. Assume that a student achieved a composition score of 84, and that the regression equation used to predict literature scores from composition scores is $\hat{Y} = 0.92X + 0.834$. If the standard error of estimate is 3.11, what is the probability that this student will achieve a literature score of at least 80?

8. What is meant by the terminology *method of least squares?*

9. Under what condition(s) do the two regression lines coincide?

10. Prediction of Y from X or X from Y, requires that the variables X and Y be measured on at least what scale?

11. *True or false:* $s_{x.y} = s_x$ if and only if $s_{y.x} = s_y$.

12. Assume that the equations of the regression lines are $\hat{Y} = 0.48X + 5.27$ and $\hat{X} = 1.32Y - 3.41$. Find r.

13. If the regression lines used to predict z_y from z_x and z_x from z_y are plotted on the same set of axes, will the two lines be parallel, perpendicular, or neither?

14. *True or false:* The mean of the predicted Y-scores and the mean of the actual Y-scores are generally not equal to one another.

Chapter 15 Mastery Test: Answers

1. $s_{y.x} = 1.82$

2. false

3. 5

4. true

5. true

6. $r = \pm 1$

7. $\hat{Y} = 78.11$
   $z = 0.608$
   Probability $= 0.7284$

8. $\Sigma(\hat{Y} - Y)^2$ is held to a minimum; that is, the sum of squares of the vertical distances from the data points to the regression line is held to a minimum.

9. The two regression lines coincide when a perfect relationship exists between variables X and Y ($r = \pm 1$).

10. interval scale

11. true

12. $r = 0.796$

13. neither

14. false